MATH WIZARDRY *for* KIDS

Margaret Kenda and Phyllis S. Williams

Illustrated by Tim Robinson

SCHOLASTIC INC.
New York Toronto London Auckland Sydney

For George Snowdeal Cunningham (1909–1993)
the best of the math wizards

• • • •

Professor Emeritus of the University of Maine,
mathematician, master chess player, newspaper columnist,
textbook author, husband, father, grandfather, teacher, and
to us, neighbor, friend, and wise counselor

• • • •

And with special thanks to our favorite math wizards—
to Marilyn Messer, to Bethany Ntacyo, Michel Ntacyo,
and Tony Williams, and to the Kenda
family: Bill, Mary, Ann, and John

ISBN 0-590-03266-6

12 11 10 9 8 7 6 5   0 1 2 3/0

Printed in the U.S.A.   23
First Scholastic printing, February 1998

CONTENTS

iii

THINK LIKE A MATH WIZARD

*T*his is your chance to become a math wizard.

When you are outdoors, you can look at a flower or a tree and discover the secret shapes and numbers that help it survive.

You can chart the patterns and shapes of your own body.

If you like art, this is your chance to construct your own designs. Decorate your room with your own floating mobile or your own shining stars.

If you're a math wizard, you can make up your own games and construct your own puzzles. You can even build your own calculator.

You can count as high as anyone has ever counted. You can find a mystery number. (Almost everyone uses it, but no one has ever discovered how it ends.) You can amaze your friends with math shortcuts.

You can perform magic tricks, figure out the chances for the future, predict wins and losses in sports.

You can glimpse other worlds where up is down and in is out. You can put your imagination into another dimension.

Just for fun, you can figure out lucky numbers. You can even give a wizard's party.

After all, you're a math wizard.

GUIDELINES FOR YOUNG MATH WIZARDS

1. *Keep an observation notebook.* Go outside, and draw the patterns and designs you see around you. You'll discover a few of nature's best secrets.

2. *Have fun with math.* Don't be afraid to make some mistakes along the way. You're always learning something about the puzzles and mysteries of the world.

3. *Keep things organized.* Before starting a project, collect all the tools and materials you'll need. When you've finished, put things back where they belong.

4. *Before you begin a project, read the steps all the way through.* Make sure you understand everything you need to do. If, after reading over a project, you don't understand every detail, try carrying out one step at a time in order. That way, you'll see the project develop as you go.

5. *Keep things safe and clean.* You don't want to leave anything around that could hurt small children or pets. A math wizard needs sharp and pointed objects, like pencils and craft knives, and sometimes uses paints and other messy things that can spill. Be sure to keep these materials out of the reach of small children.

Use only art materials with a "nontoxic" label. Usually, when you need glue, it's best to use a household glue, glue stick, or school paste rather than super or instant glue. Also, for extra safety, water-based marking pens are preferable to permanent markers.

6. *Don't be afraid to memorize.* If you know some useful facts, they'll help you to figure out some other things quickly. Learn the basics of math, and then you'll be free to get into the fun parts of math wizardry.

7. *Let your imagination run free.* Math leads you into different dimensions. You're the math wizard, and wizards need to know about mysteries, puzzles, and secrets.

TOOLS FOR MATH WIZARDS

*H*ere are tools to help you become a math wizard:

1. Plenty of plain paper, graph paper, and construction paper.
2. Pencils, (You'll also want a pencil sharpener on hand.)
3. A ruler.
4. A drawing compass.
5. A protractor. (Either kind is good, but you may find a full-circle more useful than a half-circle protractor.)
6. A triangle.
7. A calculator.
8. An observation notebook.
9. Scissors, coloring pens, and other arts and crafts supplies.
10. A directional compass for working on maps.

FOR
PARENTS
AND TEACHERS

Encouraging math is a struggle. Parents and teachers want children to know the math basics without returning to the repetitive "drill and kill" math of the past.

But math can become exciting. Think of math as the shapes, patterns, and relationships of the real world. Think of math as art and creativity.

Here are some ideas to help your children see the real-life math that they will love:

1. **Make math hands-on.** In a world full of commercial games and puzzles, help children to make their own. They can put together their own good luck puzzles, create personal math cards, or invent their own logic games.

    Have them put aside electronic calculators from time to time, and help them to create a calculator of their own, an abacus, or a math-whiz triangle.

2. **Take math outside.** Walk outside with children to study the patterns of a seashell, a pine cone, or a pussywillow. Look at the geometry that makes a spiderweb so strong. Predict a count of daisy petals. Gaze at the symmetry of a butterfly's wings or of a horse in full gallop.

3. **Take math on vacation.** One of the joys of a trip is to see (and perhaps sketch) the shapes and patterns of a beautiful landscape. A vacation may give you the opportunity to

admire the night sky or the golden proportions of historic buildings. Decades later, a child may still remember standing with you to contemplate the vast distances and inscrutable patterns of the heavens.

4. **Encourage kids to keep a sketch book and observations notebook.** Parents and English teachers often suggest the idea of keeping a journal as soon as a child can write. Now science and math teachers are seeing what a good idea it is for children to sketch and write about what they see.

5. **Make charts and graphs with your children.** Charts and graphs seem to fascinate children, whether they are tracking their own rates of growth, the local weather, a school softball game, donations to a charity, or the completion of household tasks.

6. **Encourage an interest in architecture.** Most kids like to draw plans for their room, a house, a kitchen, or a school. They may also like the idea of drawing plans for a garden, a treasure hunt, an ancient pyramid, a spaceship, or a castle.

7. **Keep sport stats.** Children who don't usually like math may enjoy keeping complicated statistics based on their own activities or on favorite teams. They may enjoy using statistics to make predictions, to explain improvement, or to take the sting out of a slump.

8. **Play with codes.** A teacher or parent can send an affectionate message or a joke in code. Your children might send you a message in return, possibly in a more complicated code. An older child may devise a personal code for a private diary.

9. **Take math into the kitchen.** Measure and divide the ingredients for a favorite recipe. Cut across an apple, and see the star at its core. Count the segments of a chili pepper or a zucchini. Make gelatine tesselations in three colors, and display on a serving plate.

10. **Make math a holiday event.** Make a holiday mobile or mosaic. Cut out stars or snowflakes for holiday decorations. Holiday handicrafts give children an opportunity to explore design, balance, symmetry, and measurement.

11. **Throw a math party.** You can help children map out a treasure hunt or celebrate a birthday by shaping a cake into numbers.

12. **Go out of your way to encourage girls and minority young people to enjoy math.** Multi-cultural math is everywhere, almost inescapable. Play a counting game that once brought peace along the Congo River. Play with the triangles of a Zuni rainbird. Look at the attempts of people all around the world to calculate pi. Work with magic squares or tangrams from China.

    A child who likes to sew might learn about geometry through thread-designs, a quilted pillow, or a personally designed book. Young people who like music may enjoy sketching the rhythms and rhymes of a jazz poem, a rap song, a folk dance, or even an old jump rope chant.

13. **Encourage math activities, without necessarily using the word *math*.** In the way that children sometimes decide they hate spinach before they ever taste spinach, they sometimes decide to avoid math before they have any real idea about math.

    Even a math-phobic kid, though, can color a homemade puzzle, play a calculator trick, or wonder over the proportions of angels in the snow. Young people who lack self-esteem may particularly benefit from personal projects such as tracing their own proportions or drawing the spiral of their own beginning lives.

14. **Encourage students with verbal ability to see the connections to math.** Sometimes the most articulate and creative students come to think that they don't need

math. They get the impression that verbal ability is the opposite of mathematical ability.

Encourage the precocious poet to learn the math of poetic meter. The natural wordsmith may be interested in palindromes, codes, or magic squares. A young artist should try a creative circle machine or 3-D shapes that fly.

15. **Don't step in too fast.** Don't solve math problems for children too quickly, or criticize their mistakes too readily. The concept is more important than the details.

16. **Don't be reluctant to expose children to difficult concepts.** Often, children seem naturally curious about the number of atoms in their own bodies, the distances to the stars, or the never ending digits of pi. Share with children the fascination of fractals, the complicated proportions of nature, the wonder of googols and the other meganumbers.

When young people feel the thrill of discovering and creating, then they will grow up loving mathematics.

1. LOOK FOR SHAPES AND PATTERNS OUTSIDE

Maybe you think that math can be learned only in a classroom, but that's not true. You can also learn math outdoors from the best teacher of all, our own earth.

Go outside, and you'll see a multitude of shapes and patterns. Would you like to look at nature's shapes and patterns up close, to sketch them, and then to find some of them in the names of lakes, mountains, and other places?

SKETCH NATURE'S SHAPES

You may live in a crowded city. You may live some place with lots of open space, near fields or a desert. You may live within the boundaries of mountains or rivers.

You may live on a prairie or by an ocean where it seems as though you can see forever.

Because of where you live, you may think of space as lines and boxes, rectangles and triangles, all closed and complicated spaces. Or you may see space as circles, arcs, and wide-open areas.

One reason people like to go on vacation is to enjoy other patterns and places, all beautiful but all different.

Go outside with a pad of paper. Find a landscape you like and sketch just the shapes you see.

Don't draw trees, for instance. Draw the rectangular, circular, or triangular shapes of the trees.

Don't draw mountains or rocks or hills. Draw their shapes.

Don't draw waterways or fields. Draw their angles.

You may want to color your shapes. Most landscapes have natural colors that repeat as the shapes and patterns repeat. Don't search for the exact colors. Just keep the general pattern of the colors in mind.

YOU MAY FIND THAT YOU HAVE MADE A VERY BEAUTIFUL AND DIFFERENT SORT OF DRAWING. WHAT HAVE YOU INCLUDED? PERHAPS YOU HAVE DISCOVERED SOME OF NATURE'S MOST INTERESTING SHAPES.

FIND NATURE NAMES

Other people have looked at the sizes and shapes around them, too. Sometimes they feel very proud to live near the biggest, the deepest, the highest, or the most peculiar shapes of nature.

Have you noticed how often mountains, rivers, lakes, plains, and other places are named for their shapes and sizes?

You can find examples where you live and whenever you travel. Here are just a few:

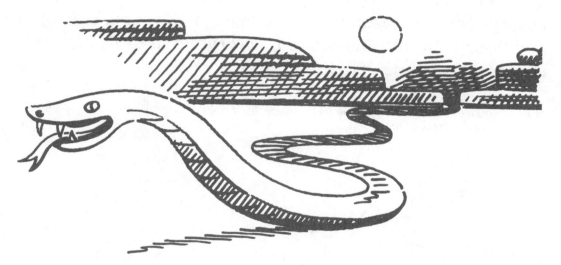

- Snake River, Idaho
- Moosehead Lake, Maine
- Breadloaf Mountain, Vermont
- Mammoth Caves, Kentucky
- The Golden Triangle (in Pittsburgh, Pennsylvania, where three rivers, the Allegheny, the Ohio, and the Monongahela, flow together into a triangle of water)
- The Big Island of Hawaii

FINDING SHAPE NAMES IS A GOOD VACATION PROJECT.

11

2. CREATE A MULTITUDE OF SHAPES

*P*erhaps you'd like to transform nature's shapes and patterns into designs of your own.

Most of the projects in this section are fun for people of any age. For this reason, you could invite both your grandmother and your little brother to help. Everyone likes to play with shapes and patterns.

Hint: *If you want help with drawing basic shapes and angles, turn to pages 312–316 in the Appendix at the back of this book.*

. . . .
BEGIN WITH A SERIOUS INSIDE SANDBOX
. . . .

A serious inside sandbox is a good way to experiment with shapes, angles, and patterns. You can draw all you want, and you can't make a mistake.

An inside sandbox is also a good way to learn to use a drawing compass. You can even make your own drawing compass.

We're counting on you to keep things clean.

Here's what you need:

A large, sturdy container such as a big
plastic box or a plastic dishpan, OR a
smaller container such as a baking
tray or jelly roll pan
Cornstarch or clean sand
A spray bottle of water
A ruler or flat stick
String
Two short sticks or pencils
A drawing compass, if you wish

Here's how to set up and use your sandbox:

1. Fill the container with the cornstarch or clean sand. (If you save the box or bag it comes in, you can use the cornstarch or sand to draw shapes and patterns another day.)

2. Spray the cornstarch or sand lightly with the water, and wipe it smooth with the ruler or flat stick.

3. To make your own drawing compass, cut a short piece of the string, slightly less than half the width of your sandbox. Tie a short stick or pencil on each end. Put one stick or pencil into the sand, and use the other as one leg of the compass.

If you wish, you can also experiment with a drawing compass that you buy.

4. Draw shapes and patterns with the drawing compass or with sticks, rulers, or even your fingers. When you want to try new shapes and patterns, just spray the cornstarch or sand with water, and wipe it smooth.

5. Important: Remember that cleaning up is part of the job.

NOW YOU CAN DRAW ALL THE CIRCLES, CURVES, AND MANY-SIDED SHAPES YOU WANT. YOU CAN TRY DIFFERENT ANGLES, AND SEE HOW THE SHAPES CHANGE. YOU CAN FIT SHAPES TOGETHER AND DESIGN YOUR OWN PUZZLES.

DESIGN A THREE-SIDED CAT

Perhaps, as a beginning wizard, you would like to create a mysterious cat companion by using triangles.

You can draw your cat either on paper or in your inside sandbox. Either way, you'll need a wide assortment of triangles.

You'll need a large, wide triangle for the body, and a smaller triangle for the head. You'll need narrow triangles for the whiskers and tail. You'll need small triangles for the eyes and even smaller triangles for the pupils of the eyes.

A Three-Sided Cat

. . . .

DESIGN A THREE-SIDED CAT
continued

Here's what you need:

Sand (in your sand box), paper, or colored construction paper

A pencil

A ruler

A protractor

Scissors and paste, if you wish

Here's how to make your cat from triangles:

1. Begin with a body for your cat. With the ruler, draw a line in the sand or on the paper. That's the base line for a triangle.

2. Use the protractor to measure angles for different types of triangles. (If you need help in using the protractor, turn to page 312 in the Appendix.)

3. If you want a cat of many colors, draw triangles on construction paper of different colors. Cut the triangles out, and paste them onto a large piece of construction paper.

YOU MAY BE SURPRISED AT THE NUMBER OF TRIANGLES NEEDED TO MAKE JUST ONE CAT. CAN YOU FIND ANY TRIANGLES ON A REAL CAT?

DISCOVER THE SECRETS OF A THREE-SIDED CAT

You probably used some very special triangles to design your cat. Now find out the secrets they hold.

Here's how to use your cat to discover triangle secrets:

1. Each of your cat triangles has three sides and three angles, but that may not be all they have in common.

   You can use a protractor to measure the three angles of each of your triangles. Add the number of degrees for all three angles of your biggest triangle. Add the three angles of your smallest triangle. Try a medium triangle.

   Have you discovered something else that is the same for every triangle? Look for the answer on page 34 at the end of this section.

2. If you know the number of degrees for two angles in a triangle, you can figure out the third angle.

   Add the two angles. Then subtract the sum from 180. That's the number of degrees in the third angle.

3. Does one of your triangles have two sides of equal length?

   If so, you can discover that two or perhaps all three of the angles are the same. Use a protractor to find out.

This special triangle, with two equal sides and two or three equal angles, is an isosceles triangle.

4. Does one of your triangles have two sides of equal length plus a 60-degree angle?

   If so, you have created a very special triangle. You'll find that each of the three angles measures 60 degrees, and all three sides are of equal length.

   This special triangle is an equilateral triangle. All the sides are equal, and so are all the angles.

YOU'RE ON YOUR WAY TO UNLOCKING TRIANGLE SECRETS. THERE ARE MANY MORE TO DISCOVER.

· · · · · · · · · ·
LEARN THE STORY OF RAINBIRDS
· ·

The mysterious Zuni rainbird is not supposed to look like a real bird. It's all shapes and lines. The body is a triangle. The head is a circle. The beak and wings are simple curves.

Yet the rainbird has power as a symbol for the Zuni people. The Zunis are one tribe of the Pueblo peoples of the western United States. They live mostly in a very dry area of New Mexico.

Perhaps because the people are often in need of rain, the rainbird has survived for centuries as one of their favorite pottery designs.

The mystery of the rainbird design lies in the triangle of the body. As the triangle takes various forms, the bird is tilted at different angles.

A tilt of the body triangle can mean that the bird is calling for rain, or that a thirsty bird lies sick from lack of rain. It can mean that a happy bird is soaked through with rain.

Lines in the design represent far-off rain, falling like stripes from the sky.

IN A DRY PLACE WHERE PEOPLE PRAY FOR RAIN, THE RAINBIRD IS A LOVED SYMBOL.

CREATE YOUR OWN RAINBIRDS

Draw your own rainbirds on paper or in your sandbox.

Here's what you need:

Sand (in your sandbox), or plain paper, graph paper, or construction paper

A pencil

A protractor, whole-circle or half-circle

A ruler

Scissors and paste, if you wish

Here's what you do:

1. Draw a rainbird with an equilateral triangle for its body. An equilateral triangle has three equal angles and three sides of equal length.

2. Draw a rainbird with a right triangle for its body. A right triangle has one right angle, an angle that measures 90 degrees.

3. Draw a rainbird with an isosceles triangle for its body. An isosceles triangle has two sides of equal length.

4. Draw a rainbird with a scalene triangle for its body. In a scalene triangle, all three angles are different, and all three sides are of different lengths.

5. If you wish, draw shapes for the rainbirds on construction paper, cut them out, and paste them onto a sheet of construction paper or posterboard.

YOU MAY WANT TO TRY OTHER RAINBIRDS. YOU'LL SEE THE DIFFERENCE. EACH RAINBIRD PROJECTS A SEPARATE PERSONALITY AND A DIFFERENT SORT OF POWER.

CREATE YOUR OWN RAINBIRDS
continued

A rainbird calling for rain:
an equilateral triangle

A happy rainbird:
a right triangle

A dancing rainbird:
a scalene triangle

A thirsty rainbird:
an isosceles triangle

**Four Different Rainbirds Made From
Four Different Triangles**

. . . .

DESIGN SHADOWS

. . . .

Draw a triangle on paper or in the sand, any size and type you wish. Then draw its shadow from one side.

The shadow you're drawing is another triangle that shares one side of the first triangle and is the same size. Draw the shadow as an exact image of the first triangle.

You have just discovered another triangle secret: doubling a triangle usually creates a four-sided shape.

Go on to find special four-sided shapes you can create with triangle shadows.

All these four-sided shapes are parallelograms (diagram 1). They all have opposite angles that are equal. They all have opposite sides that are equal. But all parallelograms are not the same.

Here's how to create four-sided shapes from triangles:

1. Draw a right triangle. That's a triangle with one right angle, an angle that measures 90 degrees.

   Look at the longest side of the right triangle. That's the hypotenuse. At the hypotenuse, draw a mirror-image shadow for the right triangle.

   You've just created a rectangle (diagram 2).

2. Draw another right triangle. Create a right angle and make the two shorter sides equal.

Draw a shadow at the hypotenuse, and see what you create.

No matter what size your right triangle is, drawing the shadow makes a square (diagram 3).

On a square, all four sides have the same measure, and all four angles measure the same.

3. From either one of the shorter sides, draw another shadow for the right triangle.

   Notice that this shape, even though it's tilted, is still a parallelogram (diagram 4). You can prove it by measuring two

DESIGN SHADOWS
continued

opposite angles and measuring two opposite sides.

4. Draw an equilateral triangle. That's a triangle with equal sides and equal angles. All the angles measure 60 degrees.

   Draw a shadow of an equilateral triangle in any direction, and you've created a rhombus (diagram 5). Measure each side, and see what's special about a rhombus.

5. Solve another mystery. Can you draw a shadow for any triangle in a way that does not create a four-sided shape? Look on page 34 at the end of this section for the answer.

LOOK AT REAL SHADOWS THE NEXT TIME YOU GO OUTDOORS ON A SUNNY DAY. YOU'LL FIND THAT A SHADOW IS NOT THE SAME SIZE OR SHAPE AS THE REAL THING.

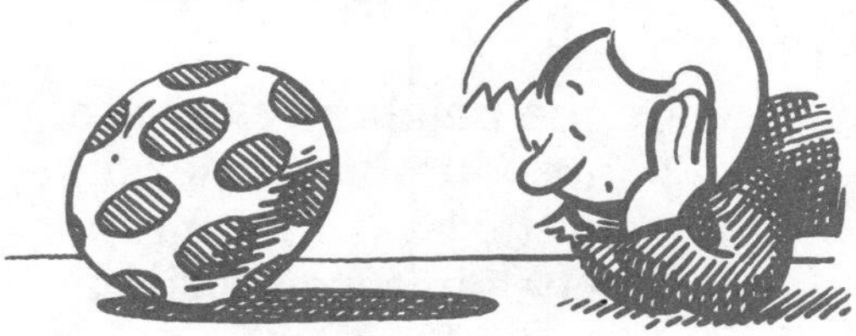

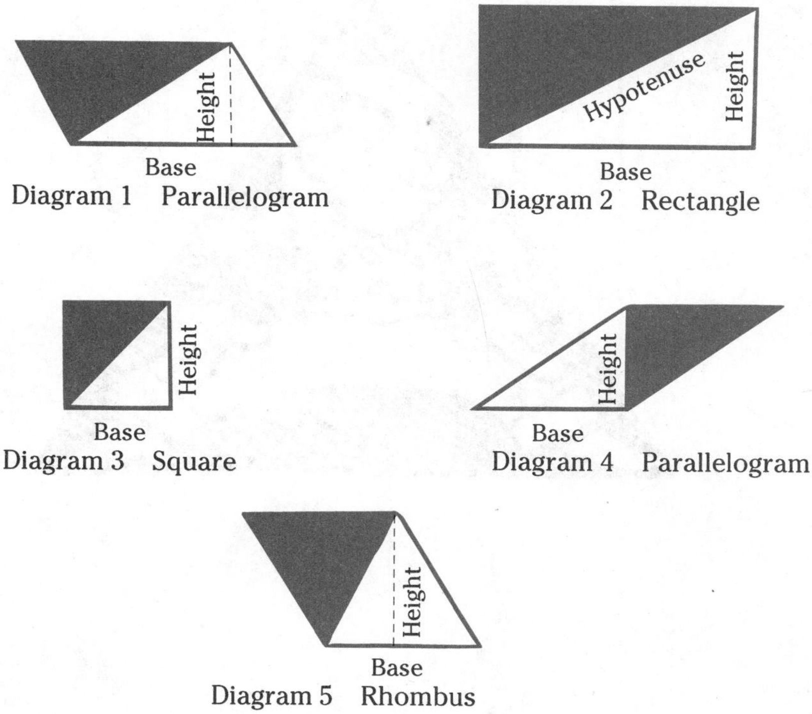

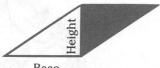

Height
Base
Diagram 1 Parallelogram
Hypotenuse
Height
Base
Diagram 2 Rectangle
Height
Base
Diagram 3 Square
Height
Base
Diagram 4 Parallelogram
Height
Base
Diagram 5 Rhombus

Triangles and Their Shadows

DISCOVER A THREE-SIDED AND FOUR-SIDED SECRET

You can use a triangle shadow to find the area of a triangle, that is, the total amount of space inside the triangle.

Here's how to measure the space inside a triangle:

1. Measure the base of any one of the four-sided figures you created by drawing a shadow of a triangle.

2. Measure the height of the four-sided figure. That's the measurement from the base to the top line. (The height forms a right angle with the base.)

3. Multiply the two numbers. The result is the area of the whole four-sided figure in square inches or square centimeters.

4. Divide by 2. Now you've found the area of one of the triangles. State your answer in square inches or square centimeters.

: **YOU'VE JUST DISCOVERED ONE**
: **MORE TRIANGLE SECRET.**

DESIGN YOUR OWN FOUR-SIDED SHAPES

You may think that four-sided shapes are solid, sensible, and mostly square. You may be in for a surprise.

You know that you can make a shadow for most kinds of triangles, and end up with a parallelogram.

Now try it the other way around. See whether you can draw a four-sided shape that you cannot divide into two equal three-sided shapes.

Hint: Begin by drawing two parallel lines. They're two sides of your four-sided shape. Then draw the other two sides any which way.

You've just created your own unique four-sided design. Perhaps it looks something like these:

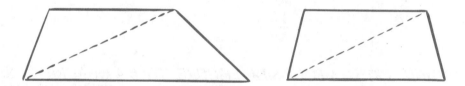

Trapezoids

DESIGN YOUR OWN FOUR-SIDED SHAPES
continued

Now see whether you can draw another wobbly four-sided figure. This time draw one with no parallel lines and no equal angles.

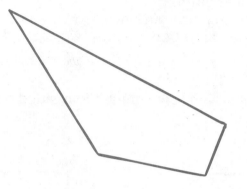

YOUR DESIGN IS STILL A FOUR-SIDED FIGURE, STILL A QUADRILATERAL. THE WORD FORM QUADR *MEANS "FOUR."* LATERAL *MEANS "SIDE" OR "SIDEWAYS." THIS ONE CERTAINLY GOES SIDEWAYS.*

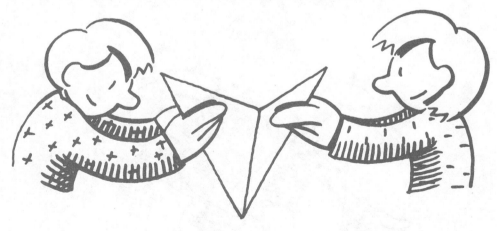

DESIGN FIVE-SIDED SHAPES AND STARS

You won't be surprised to learn that the word form *penta* means "five." The Pentagon in Washington, D.C., is headquarters for the U.S. Department of Defense. It's the largest office building in the world, and it's called the Pentagon because it has five very long sides.

A five-sided shape is a pentagon. A five-pointed star that you can draw inside a pentagon is a pentagram, a shape formed of five lines.

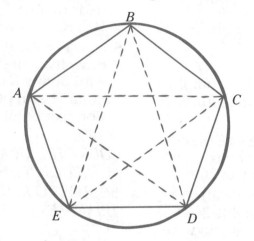

A Pentagon with a Pentagram Drawn Inside

By the way, the stars in the sky are not really pentagrams. People just like to draw them that way.

You can design a pentagon of your own, and use it to make five-pointed stars.

· · · · · · · · · · ·

DESIGN FIVE-SIDED SHAPES AND STARS
continued

Here's what you need:

Graph paper or plain paper
A pencil
A drawing compass
A protractor
A ruler
A calculator

Here's what you do:

1. First, use the drawing compass to draw an outer circle for your pentagon.

2. Next figure out the size of the angle you need to create a five-sided shape inside the circle.

    You know that a circle always has 360 degrees. Divide 360 by 5. (Use a calculator if you wish.) The answer, 72, is the number of degrees you need to divide the circle into five equal parts.

3. Use the protractor and the drawing compass to mark the circle every 72 degrees. You'll have five marks. Label the marks *A*, *B*, *C*, *D*, and *E*.

4. Draw the pentagon. Use the ruler to draw lines from *A* to *B* to *C* to *D* to *E*.

5. Now draw a star. Use the ruler to draw five lines. Connect point *A* with points *C* and *D*. Connect point *B* with points *D* and *E*. Connect point *C* with point *E*.

COUNT THE TRIANGLES INSIDE THE FIVE SIDES OF THE PENTAGON. BE SURE TO LOOK FOR HIDDEN TRIANGLES.

DESIGN SIX-SIDED SHAPES AND STARS

You can design your own six-sided shape, a hexagon, and then draw a hexagram inside it. A hexagram, or six-pointed star, is a figure formed of six lines. You've seen it before. It's the star of David.

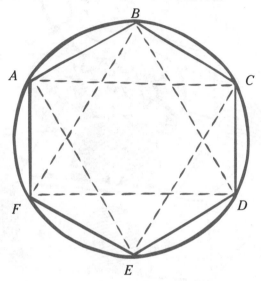

A Hexagon with a Hexagram Drawn Inside

Here's what you need:

Graph paper or plain paper
A pencil
A drawing compass
A ruler

Here's how to draw a hexagon inside a circle:

1. Use the drawing compass to draw a circle.

2. Figure out the size of the angle you need to create a six-sided shape inside the circle. Divide the number of degrees in a circle, 360, by 6. The answer, 60, is the number of degrees you need to divide the circle into six equal parts.

3. Use the protractor and drawing compass to mark the circle every 60 degrees. You'll have six marks, *A*, *B*, *C*, *D*, *E*, and *F*.

4. Draw the hexagon. Use your ruler to draw lines from *A* to *B* to *C* to *D* to *E* to *F*.

5. Now draw a six-pointed star inside the hexagon. Notice you've formed two overlapping triangles.

· · · · · · · · · · ·

DESIGN SIX-SIDED SHAPES AND STARS
continued

WHAT IF YOU DESIGNED A GREAT BUILDING LIKE THE PENTAGON BUT WITH SIX SIDES? IMAGINE WHERE YOU WOULD PUT THE DOORS AND WINDOWS. EVEN BETTER, IMAGINE HOW THE INSIDE ROOMS WOULD LOOK. YOU MIGHT EVEN CREATE A STAR-SHAPED ROOM.

· · · · · · · · · ·

DISCOVER A SIX-SIDED SECRET

· ·

You don't need to measure angles to construct a six-sided figure.

Here's another way:

1. Draw a circle. Then open your compass as wide as the radius of the circle is long, and keep it that way. (The radius is a line from the center point of the circle to the outer rim.)

2. Make a mark on the rim of the circle. Place the metal tip of the compass on that mark. Swing an arc to one side, and make a mark where the arc crosses the rim of the circle. Now swing an arc to the other side, and again make a mark where the arc crosses.

3. Place the metal tip of the compass on one of the two marks you made in step 2. Swing an arc, and make a new mark where the arc crosses the rim of the circle.

4. Mark all the way around the circle the same way. When you finish, you will have divided the perimeter of the circle into six equal parts.

5. Connect the marks to form a six-sided figure.

You're discovering a six-sided secret: The radius of the circle is equal in length to each of the six part divisions. You can keep your compass open at the same measurement all the way around.

Why didn't you need to measure?

Hint: As you draw lines from the center point of the circle to the rim, you're creating triangles. Equilateral triangles have three sides the same and three angles the same. Each angle measures 60 degrees.

WHILE YOU WERE CONSTRUCTING A SIX-SIDED FIGURE, YOU WERE ALSO CONSTRUCTING EQUILATERAL TRIANGLES. EACH TRIANGLE HAS THREE 60-DEGREE ANGLES AND THREE EQUAL SIDES.

DESIGN EIGHT-SIDED SHAPES AND STARS

An octopus has eight tentacles. You can design an "octopus house" that has eight sides and contains an eight-pointed star. You'll be creating an octagon with an octagram inside.

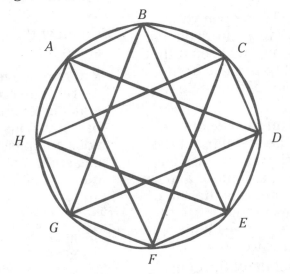

An Octagon with an Octagram Drawn Inside

Here's what you need:

Graph paper or plain paper
A pencil
A drawing compass
A protractor
A ruler

Here's how to draw an octagon inside a circle:

1. Use the drawing compass to draw a circle.

2. Figure the size of the angle you need to create an eight-sided shape inside the circle.

   You know that a circle always has 360 degrees. Divide 360 by 8. The answer, 45, is the number of degrees you need to divide the circle into eight equal parts.

3. Use the protractor and the drawing compass to mark the rim of the circle every 45 degrees. You'll have eight equal parts.

4. Use your ruler to draw lines from one point to the next, all around the circle. Now you have an octagon.

5. To draw a star, connect every point with the third point away from it: *A* with *D*, *B* with *E*, and so on. You'll go around the circle twice and end up at the beginning with a true eight-pointed star.

DESIGN EIGHT-SIDED SHAPES AND STARS
continued

6. If you like, go on to connect all the other points. Then you'll have three overlapping squares.

7. Design figures with nine or more sides. For a nine-sided figure, divide the number of degrees in a circle, 360, by 9. The answer, 40, tells you where to mark the rim of your circle. To create a figure with ten sides, divide 360 by 10. Or create a figure with twelve sides.

YOU CAN GO ON AND ON. JUST MAKE SURE TO CHOOSE NUMBERS THAT DIVIDE INTO 360 DEGREES EVENLY, AND DRAW YOUR CIRCLES BIG ENOUGH TO LEAVE ROOM FOR ALL THE SIDES YOU'LL NEED. YOU CAN DRAW A STAR FOR EACH FIGURE, TOO.

DISCOVER A SECRET ABOUT A
TWELVE-POINTED STAR

If you create a figure with twelve sides, you may find that it's beginning to look a lot like a circle.

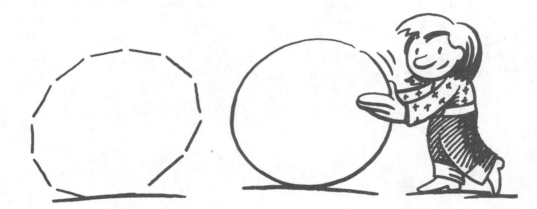

THE MORE LINES YOU USE, THE CLOSER YOU GET TO A CIRCLE.

MAKE YOUR STARS SHINE

Paint your stars with glow-in-the-dark paint, or spread glitter glue on your stars.

Perhaps you could decorate the ceiling or walls of your room. (Be sure to get your parents' permission. Your parents might prefer that you put up the stars with removable tape.)

NOW YOU CAN HAVE YOUR OWN SHINING STARS. JUST DECIDE WHETHER YOU WANT THEM FIVE POINTS, SIX POINTS, EIGHT POINTS, OR EVEN MORE. OR YOU MIGHT LIKE TO MIX THEM.

ANSWERS FOR SECTION 2:
CREATE A MULTITUDE OF SHAPES

Discover the Secrets of a Three-Sided Cat:

Step 1. If you measure three angles of any triangle and then add them, you'll find that the sum is always 180 degrees.

Design Shadows:

Step 5. Here's one way (perhaps you can think of another way) to double a triangle and not create a four-sided shape. Take a right triangle. Extend one of the legs of the right angle and draw a shadow. You'll create a three-sided figure twice as large as the original.

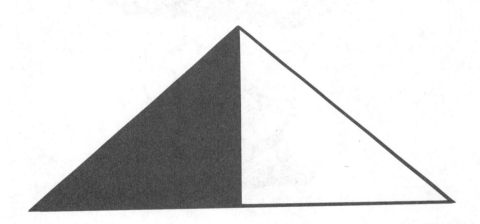

3. DESIGN CREATIVE CIRCLES AND SURPRISE SHAPES

Here's your chance to design creative shapes. You may be surprised when you come up with some very odd designs.

MAKE YOUR OWN CREATIVE CIRCLE MACHINE

You can draw circles in your inside sandbox. You can draw circles on paper with your drawing compass. Or you can take a new approach. You can draw circles with your own creative circle machine. These won't be just ordinary circles. They will be creative circle, curve, and spiral designs.

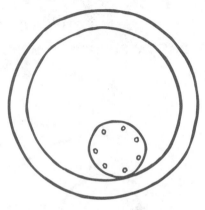

A Creative Circle Machine

Here's what you need:

*Fine corrugated cardboard or
    laminated posterboard
A drawing compass
Scissors or a craft knife
An emery board or nail file
Construction paper or posterboard
Removable tape
Ballpoint pens in different colors*

Here's what to do:

1. Use the drawing compass to construct a circle out of the cardboard. Your circle can be any size (at least 6 inches [15 or 16 centimeters] across) as long as it will fit onto a piece of construction paper or posterboard.

. . . .

MAKE YOUR OWN CREATIVE CIRCLE MACHINE
continued

Draw an inner circle so that your circle has a rim about 2 inches (5 or 6 centimeters) thick.

2. Use the drawing compass to construct small designing circles out of the cardboard:

• A circle about 3 inches (7 or 8 centimeters) in diameter

• A circle about 2 inches (5 or 6 centimeters) in diameter

• A circle about 1 inch (2 or 3 centimeters) in diameter

• For even more interesting designs, you might also want to cut out other shapes, for example, a small football shape about 2 inches (5 or 6 centimeters) long

3. Use the scissors or craft knife to cut out the big circle, its inner circle, and the small designing shapes you made in step 2.

: *Caution: You need adult help in*
: *cutting cardboard.*

4. Use scissors or the metal tip of the drawing compass to punch several small holes around the small designing shapes. Enlarge these holes until they are about $1/4$ inch (0.5 centimeter) across.

5. Use the emery board or nail file to smooth both the inner and outer edges of the large circle. Also smooth the rim of the small designing shapes.

6. Use removable tape to tape the large circle onto construction paper or posterboard.

Here's how to make designs:

1. Place a small shape inside the large circular hole against the rim. Insert a ballpoint pen into one of the holes in the small shape. Turn the small circle around and around so that it bumps again and again into the inside rim of the large circle.

2. Use ballpoint pens in different colors to give your designs new looks.

3. If you wish, remove the large circle and tape it to another part of the paper or on another sheet of paper.

: YOU'LL GET CIRCLES, CURVES,
: ELLIPSES, ALL INTERCONNECTED IN
: ONE DESIGN AFTER ANOTHER.

. . . .

CREATE A TROUBLESOME DESIGN

. . . .

You can create a strange design that mathematicians quarreled over for years.

Of course, most mathematicians are good and honest people. In this case, however, each mathematician wanted the honor of discovering this design. Some tried to be the first to publish the design and then quarreled about the dates of publication. Some even tried to steal the design from others.

Yet you may never have heard of the design that caused all this trouble. It's called a cycloid.

You can design a cycloid of your own. But please stay friendly and polite while you do it.

Drawing a cycloid is tricky, but it's also fun. Even if you don't get the design perfect, you can still see how a cycloid looks.

Here's what you need:

Paper

A small circle with a ballpoint pen in it from your creative circle machine

A block, box, or two rulers

Here's what you do:

1. Place the small circle with the pen in it from your creative circle machine on a piece of paper so that the pen is ready to draw.

2. Put down the block or box, and hold the pen and circle firmly against it, or else hold the circle between two rulers. Either way, you may want to get someone to help you hold it steady.

3. Now roll the circle along the straight bottom edge of the block, box, or rulers. As the circle moves around, the pen needs to stay in the same place. The pen ought to make a mark on the paper in the form of an arc.

The arc has secrets. No matter how big or small you designed the arc, its length will always be four times the length of the diameter of the rolling circle. Also, the area under the arc will always be three times the area of the rolling circle.

In this case, the diameter of the circle is the distance from the hole for the pen to a point on the opposite rim.

· · · · · · · · · · ·

CREATE A TROUBLESOME DESIGN

continued

You can picture a cycloid if you imagine your bicycle wheels rolling along the ground. When you are riding your bike north, half of each wheel is always rolling south. If you could attach a magic pencil to your bicycle wheel, the arc the pencil traces is a cycloid.

THESE DAYS, MATHEMATICIANS LIKE TO PLAY WITH CYCLOIDS. THEY HAVE EVEN USED THE IDEA TO DESIGN A CONTAINER. IF YOU DROP MARBLES INTO THIS CONTAINER FROM ANY POINT AND AT THE SAME TIME, THEY WILL ALWAYS ARRIVE AT THE BOTTOM AT EXACTLY THE SAME TIME. YOU MAY HAVE SEEN THIS TRICK AT A CARNIVAL OR FAIR.

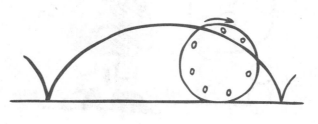

A Cycloid

LEARN A CIRCLE SECRET

Draw any number of circles. As long as they are true circles, they have something important in common: they are all round.

In fact, circles have only one way to be different. They can be different in size but in no other way.

GO ON TO UNLOCK ANOTHER CIRCLE SECRET.

MEASURE A CIRCLE

People love to measure circles. Mathematicians have been measuring circles for thousands of years. Now, with the help of computers, they're still hard at work. Perhaps you can discover why.

Here's what you need:

Objects with circular tops and bottoms, such as cups or jars

Paper and pencil

A drawing compass

A ruler

String

Scissors

Here's what you do:

1. Trace the circular bottom of one of your objects onto a piece of paper. Measure the diameter of the circle. The diameter is a line that runs straight across the circle, through the exact center.

2. Circle the round bottom of the object itself with a piece of string. Be sure the string is at an even distance from the bottom all around. Have someone cut the string where the ends meet. You're measuring the circumference of the circle, the distance all around the rim.

3. Use the ruler to measure the string. Divide the length of the string by the length of the diameter of the circle, and discover how many diameters there are in the circumference of the circle.

   Your answer should be 3 plus a little.

5. Try this same way of measuring circles of other sizes. You could be finding out a circle secret.

   The length of the circumference of a circle is always in the same ratio to the length of the diameter. That's true no matter how big or how small the circle is. The number is always the same, 3 plus a little.

   For thousands of years, people have been interested in discovering the exact number. Here's a short version of the number: about 3.141592654. The ancient Greeks named the number for the 16th letter of the Greek alphabet, pi.

PI MAY NOT BE A WHOLE NUMBER, BUT IN ITS WAY IT IS AS IMPORTANT AS WHOLE NUMBERS SUCH AS 1, 2, AND 3.

MEMORIZE A LONG NUMBER WITHOUT REALLY TRYING

Here's an easy way to remember at least some of the digits of pi. Just remember this sentence and the number of letters in each word:

FOR I KNOW I CHOSE KNOWLEDGE TO ATTAIN LIFE'S GOAL.
3 1 4   1 5   9   2   6   5   4

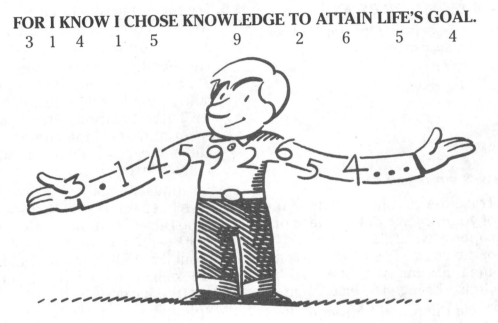

NOW YOU KNOW A MNEMONIC, THAT IS, AN EASY WAY TO JOG YOUR MEMORY. WHEN YOU SAY MNEMONIC, DON'T PRONOUNCE THE *M*.

LEARN THE STORY OF A HARD-WORKING NUMBER

Pi is a very useful number to know.

Picture measuring a bicycle tire. You could put a string around it, but you'd have a hard time taking an accurate measure. And measuring tires, even car and truck tires, would be easy compared to measuring some other circular shapes.

Suppose you want to measure spheres, cylinders, cones, and the areas inside them.

Suppose you want to measure something large and far away, such as the moon and the planets. Suppose you want to know the circumference of the earth.

Pi, which allows us to make difficult measurements, holds a certain mysterious fascination. Pi is useful, but it is also among the grand puzzles of the centuries.

From ancient times, people all over the world have worked on solving the puzzle. They want to know the exact measurement of pi. Why have all these people worked so hard for so many years?

Some people hope to discover a pattern within the decimal places of pi.

Often, mathematicians are able to invent new uses for pi.

Perhaps, however, most people work just for the challenge, in the hope that some day mysterious pi will be fully understood.

IMAGINE SOLVING THE PI PUZZLE RIGHT ALONG WITH A TEAM OF PEOPLE FROM ALL TIMES AND PLACES. GO ON TO SEE HOW TO JOIN THE TEAM.

Solve a Round-the-World Puzzle

It's as if the whole world has worked together to discover pi. Join this worldwide team.

You know that pi is about 3.14159265.

Use your calculator to see how people have figured pi over the years. See how close they came.

Here are seven ways that it has been figured:

1. Close to 4000 years ago, the ancient Babylonians figured pi at 25/8. Divide 25 by 8.

2. Ancient Egyptians wrote pi as 256/81. Divide 256 by 81.

3. Here's a puzzle from the Bible. The Old Testament recounts that King Solomon created a "molten sea," a sort of ceremonial pool for his temple. The pool was splendid, with 12 brass oxen surrounding it. The "sea" measured 10 cubits from one brim to the other. In other words, the diameter was 10 cubits. A line of 30 cubits "did compass it round about." That was the circumference. For an estimate of pi, divide 30 by 10.

4. The great mathematician of ancient Greece, Archimedes, said that pi was more than $3^{10}/71$ but less than $3^1/7$.

    Use your calculator to divide 10 by 71, and write the answer in decimal places after the 3. Then divide 1 by 7, and write the answer in decimal places after the 3.

5. The Chinese people of the fifth century figured pi as 355/113. To see how close they came, divide 355 by 113.

6. Aryabhata was a mathematician of India about 1500 years ago. He calculated pi as 62,832 over 20,000. Use your calculator to divide 62,832 by 20,000.

7. Bhaskara was a mathematician of India in about the year 1150. He calculated pi as the square root of 10. Push 10 on your calculator, then the square root symbol.

SOLVE A ROUND-THE-WORLD PUZZLE
continued

If you wish, look on page 49 at the end of this section for these mathematicians' answers to the pi puzzle.

By medieval times, an Arabian mathematician had figured pi to 16 decimal places. In 1610, a German mathematician got the answer to 35 places.

In 1873, English mathematician William Shanks published the results of many years of hard work. He figured pi to 707 decimal places. (He had no way of knowing that he had made an error at the 528th place.)

By 1948, two Americans, John W. French, Jr., and D. F. Ferguson had corrected other mathematicians' errors and figured pi to 808 places.

By 1989, the Chudnovsky brothers had it right to more than a billion decimal places.

> **NOW THAT COMPUTERS HAVE TAKEN OVER THE JOB, PI HAS BEEN FIGURED TO MILLIONS AND MILLIONS OF DECIMAL PLACES.**

READ A FRACTURED STORY

Have you ever looked in multiple mirrors where you can see an image of an image of an image? Or boxes within boxes within boxes?

Imagine an even more complicated pattern changing over and over, breaking apart and coming together again, smaller and smaller or larger and larger without end. A pattern of that sort could be a fractal.

Fractals are complicated and mysterious shapes, shapes that change and then change again.

You need a special way to describe them.

The idea of fractals is a couple of hundred years old. Benoit Mandlebrot said he named fractals from the Latin verb *frangere*, which means "to break." Fractals are shapes that, among other ways of changing, break into fragments.

You can see fractals every day. Frost on a window is a fractal. A cloud blowing in the sky can be a fractal. A fern or the root of a plant can be a fractal. Trees grow like fractals.

How do fractals work? Take a basic shape (a triangle, a snowflake, or even just a straight line), and make it grow. Make the basic shape duplicate itself again and again. The result grows more and more complicated, yet the basic shape is still there.

A strange new type of computer fractals never have a basic shape you can see. Instead, these fractals grow and change according to a mathematical formula.

READ A FRACTURED STORY
continued

Because fractals are complicated, they are useful to explain real-life complicated shapes. Fractals are good for plotting complicated movements such as those that occur in changing weather, objects in outer space, or economic trends.

A mapmaker might use fractals to describe a coastline. A movie producer might use fractals to design scenes in movies.

MODERN COMPUTERS HAVE MADE FRACTALS USEFUL, FUN, POPULAR—AND OFTEN VERY BEAUTIFUL.

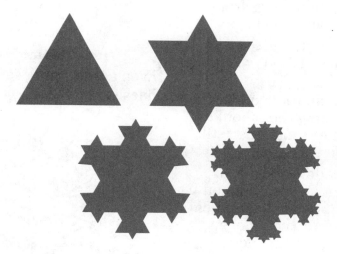

The First Four Stages of a Snowflake Fractal

The First Four Stages of a Triangle Fractal

DESIGN SURPRISE SHAPES

You can have fun creating your own sort of fractal, even without a computer.

Here's how to design a tree fractal:

1. Draw a tree with straight lines. Each time you draw a branch, draw three smaller branches from it. Then draw three still-smaller branches from each of those. Draw three twigs from each very small branch.

   Or you might draw a tree with each line curved. That will look more realistic.

2. If you wish, add roots under the ground. Each big root should lead to smaller roots, then still smaller, then very small.

3. If you wish, add leaves. You could cut out leaves from construction paper and paste them on your tree. You could even add apples or a bird's nest.

OF COURSE, YOUR DESIGN CAN-NOT GO ON FOREVER. YOU'LL WANT TO STOP SOON TO DO SOMETHING ELSE. IF YOU HAD AN INFINITELY LARGE PIECE OF PAPER AND AN INFINITELY LONG TIME (PLUS AN INFINITE ATTEN-TION SPAN), THEN YOU COULD GO ON FOREVER.

A Straight-Line Fractal Tree

Even a tree composed of straight lines is realistic.

A Curved-Line Fractal Tree

This tree is *more* realistic.

ANSWERS FOR SECTION 3: DESIGN CREATIVE CIRCLES AND SURPRISE SHAPES

Solve a Round-the-World Puzzle:

Step 1.	Babylonians	3.125
Step 2.	Egyptians	3.160
Step 3.	Old Testament	About 3
Step 4.	Archimedes	Between 3.141 and 3.142
Step 5.	Chinese	3.14159292
Step 6.	Aryabhata	3.1416
Step 7.	Bhaskara	3.16227

Compare these answers to 3.14159265.

4. FIND OUT NATURE'S SECRET SHAPES AND PATTERNS

*N*ature's many shapes and patterns are interesting and may be complicated. You may have to look hard to see that these shapes and patterns often have something in common.

Would you like to discover a pattern that repeats from flowers to seashells, from trees to apple seeds?

Would you like to know nature's favorite numbers?

Would you like to know the shapes and patterns that help plants survive?

In this section you will learn a fascinating way to "count on nature."

THE STORY OF A MAN WHO LOVED NUMBERS

You have probably heard of the famous Leaning Tower of Pisa in Italy. A man named Leonardo was born in the same town and in the very same year, 1175, that work began on the great tower. No one knew then that the tower would lean more and more every year or that Leonardo would become an important mathematician.

In 1175, people did not have first and last names in the same way they do now. To avoid confusion, people often introduced themselves by mentioning their hometown. In books, Leonardo is sometimes called Leonardo of Pisa. The name of the town helps people tell the difference, for instance, between Leonardo of Pisa and the other very famous Leonardo, Leonardo da Vinci.

(You may be able to think of some last names used today that began as names of places.)

For a time, Leonardo's family lived in Algeria in northern Africa. Leonardo's father, Bonacci, was a customs official there.

Leonardo loved the mathematics he saw in use all around him in Algeria. He was used to counting with Roman numerals (I, V, X, C), but the Algerian people counted with the Hindu-Arabic numerals (0, 1, 2, 3, 4) that we use now.

Leonardo liked this idea very much. He decided that, when he returned home to Italy, he would write books about math, and he would teach people about these different and very useful numbers.

Leonardo also decided to give himself a new name to put on his books. Since he was the son of Bonacci, he combined part of *filius*, the Latin word for "son," with "Bonacci." That gave him his new name, Fibonacci.

Before long, Fibonacci, the son of Bonacci, discovered a sequence of numbers that helps to explain nature's math. Some people call that sequence the Fibonacci numbers. Others call it the Fascinating Fibonaccis.

If you ever go to Italy, you can visit the Leaning Tower of Pisa. Across from the tower, you will see a statue of the man who loved numbers.

GO ON TO SEE HOW THE FASCINATING FIBONACCIS WORK.

FIGURE OUT VERY BEAUTIFUL NUMBERS

You can write the Fascinating Fibonaccis in a series of numbers.

These numbers offer one way to look at nature and to discover nature's secrets.

Once you know how the numbers work, you can look for them all around you.

Here's how to count the Fascinating Fibonaccis:

If you wish, you can use a calculator to figure out these numbers. The sequence begins like this:

1, 1, 2, 3, 5, 8, … (Can you tell how to go on?)

To get the next number, add the preceding two numbers. Here's how to start:

$$0 + 1 = 1$$
$$1 + 1 = 2$$
$$1 + 2 = 3$$
$$2 + 3 = 5$$
$$3 + 5 = 8$$
$$5 + 8 = …$$

You can keep going on your own, or you can look on page 63 at the end of this section for more of the series.

The largest Fibonacci number that people have found so far has hundreds of digits. You really ought to stop long before you get that high!

GO ON TO SEE BEAUTIFUL WAYS TO USE FIBONACCI NUMBERS TO INVESTIGATE LIVING THINGS.

SEE WHO LOVES YOU

There are Fibonacci numbers everywhere in nature. Find a daisy, count the petals, and maybe you can learn something else, too.

You've probably heard that you can find out whether someone special loves you by reciting on the petals of a daisy: "She loves me/She loves me not" or "He loves me/He loves me not."

Here's a secret to make sure the daisy tells you that someone special does love you:

1. If you're lucky enough to find a perfect daisy, the number of petals it has may be a number from the Fibonacci series, usually, 13, 21, or 34.

   If you begin counting "loves me" with petal 1, then a daisy with 13 or 21 petals will always end with "loves me."

   (Of course, petals blow off and fall off. Sometimes it's hard to find a perfect daisy.)

2. If you find a perfect large daisy that looks as if it has 34 petals, you'd better start counting "loves me not" at petal 1. Otherwise, you'll end up with "loves me not," and you don't want that. This is the sort of large daisy you'd probably find growing wild in a field, not in a garden.

· · · · · · · · · · ·

SEE WHO LOVES YOU
continued

SO DAISIES DO TELL. MAYBE THEY DON'T REALLY TELL WHO LOVES YOU, BUT IF YOU'RE LUCKY, THEY CAN TELL YOU ABOUT FIBONACCI NUMBERS. TRY COUNTING OTHER FLOWER BLOSSOMS, TOO. IF YOU COUNT ENOUGH OF ANY ONE KIND OF PLANT, YOU'LL OFTEN FIND FIBONACCI NUMBERS.

COUNT ON FRUITS AND VEGETABLES

Cut open a fruit or vegetable, and count the sections inside.

For instance, count the sections inside a cucumber, a pear, a tomato, or a lemon.

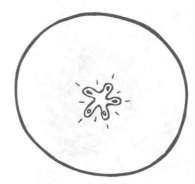

Seed cavity of a pear

Seed cavity of a cucumber

Seed cavity of a tomato

You'll probably find Fibonacci numbers such as 3, 5, and 8.

· · · · · · · · · ·

COUNT ON FRUITS AND VEGETABLES
continued

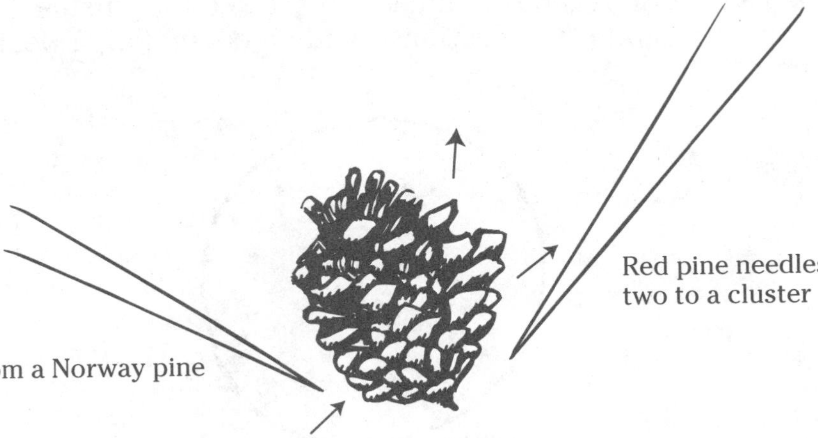

Needles from a Norway pine

Red pine needles,
two to a cluster

Cone from a Norway pine
(Arrows indicate direction of spirals.)

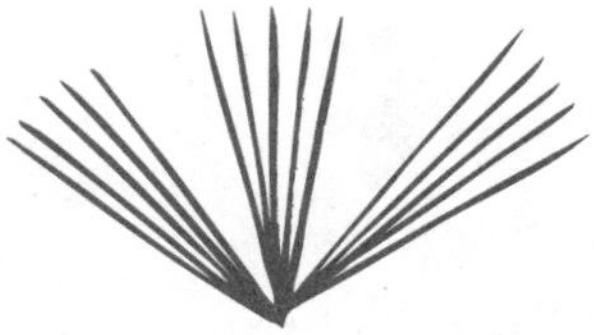

Needles from a white pine, five to a cluster

Fibonacci Numbers in Pine Needles

LOOK FOR FIBONACCI NUMBERS IN CLUSTERS OF PINE NEEDLES, TOO. YOU'LL ALMOST ALWAYS FIND PINE NEEDLES IN CLUSTERS OF 2, 3, OR 5. THOSE ARE ALL FIBONACCI NUMBERS.

COUNT ON A PINE CONE

Sometimes Fibonacci numbers are called the pine cone numbers. You can find out why.

The spirals on a pine cone are leaves of a sort. Usually, you think of leaves as soft, but pine cone leaves are hard and packed together. These hard leaves protect the pine cone in all sorts of weather.

The name for leaves of this sort is *bracts*. If you look carefully at pine cone bracts, you can see that they circle the pine cone in spirals.

The spirals overlap, but if you look very carefully, you can see two patterns of spirals.

In one pattern the spirals rise at a steep angle from the bottom to the top of the pine cone. These spirals are so steep that they are almost vertical, up and down.

In the other pattern the overlapping spirals rise gradually, round and round the pine cone. These spirals are so gradual that they are almost horizontal, nearly straight across.

Here's how to count pine cone spirals:

1. Choose several pine cones so you can compare them.

2. Beware that counting the overlapping rows is not easy. Rotate the pine cone in your hand, and touch each bract so you can follow the spirals around the pine cone.

   You can make the count easier by marking the rows with colored markers. Mark the colors directly onto the pine cone.

3. Count the gradual rows of bracts.

4. Count the steep rows of bracts.

5. Write the two numbers together as a proportion. You may be writing 3/5. You may be writing 5/8 or 8/13, or another set of Fibonacci numbers.

When you write the two numbers this way, you show how one part of the pine cone relates to another. This proportion is important. You can expect that it is part of nature's way of protecting and assuring the survival of the pine cone.

PINE CONES HAVE SOMETHING IN COMMON WITH PINEAPPLES, ARTICHOKES, PALM TREES, AND SUNFLOWERS. YOU ALMOST ALWAYS FIND THAT THE PATTERNS OCCUR IN FIBONACCI NUMBERS.

COUNT ON A PUSSYWILLOW

Count the buds on a pussywillow. You are likely to find a Fibonacci number.

Then look at how the pussywillow buds grow around the stem.

When a plant grows taller, it grows from the tip. As the tip grows, it slowly, slowly circles in the air. You'll have to imagine the tip circling as it grows. The motion is much too slow for you to see.

If you look carefully, though, you can see another circling on a pussywillow. Look at the buds, and you'll see that they grow at angles from the stem of the pussywillow. In other words, they grow in a spiral.

COUNT THE SPIRALS ON A FULL-GROWN PUSSYWILLOW. YOU MAY FIND ANOTHER FIBONACCI NUMBER.

COUNT ON A PLANT YOU GROW YOURSELF

Grow your own avocado plant, and see how it measures up. You'll need a notebook to keep track.

Here's what you need:

Seed from the center of a ripe avocado
A sauce dish, sprouter, or other small container
Water
Three toothpicks
A 6-inch to 8-inch (15- to 20-centimeter) plant pot with underdish
Old newspapers
Pebbles
Potting soil
A notebook, ruler, and pencil

Here's how to start:

1. Dry the avocado seed until you can peel off the outer covering.

2. Balance the seed on the lip of the sauce dish or other container. To do that, insert the three toothpicks around the base of the seed. The toothpicks will hold the seed above the water in the container.

   Fill the container with water until the water just reaches the base of the seed.

3. Wait for a root and two leaves to grow. Then your avocado is ready to plant in the pot.

4. To plant your avocado, cover the work surface with the old newspapers, or else take the job outside. Line the bottom of the pot with the pebbles, and then fill about halfway with the potting soil.

   Plant the avocado seed with the large end down. Water it well.

5. Keep your avocado on a windowsill or in another warm place. Keep the plant moist.

Here's how to measure the avocado as it grows:

1. About twice a week, record measurements and make sketches in your notebook. Be sure to include:
   • The date of the observation
   • The height of the plant
   • The number of leaves that sprout
   • The height of the leaves on the stem

COUNT ON A PLANT YOU GROW YOURSELF
continued

2. Make a sketch at least once a week to show:
   - The positions and angles of the leaves on the stem
   - The way the leaves spiral around the main stem

3. As the plant grows taller, count the number of leaves in each spiral around the main stem.

Here's how to count a spiral of leaves:

1. To count a whole spiral, begin with a bottom leaf that grows from the stem at a particular angle. Count that leaf as number 1. Count upward. You'll be counting leaves at different angles. Count leaves around the stem until you come to a leaf at the same angle as leaf number 1. (Don't include this last leaf in your count.) That's a whole spiral.

2. Stop and figure. You may find Fibonacci numbers in your measurements, and you may find numbers that are next to each other in the Fibonacci series.

GO ON TO SEE HOW TO KEEP YOUR AVOCADO ALIVE AND HOW FIBONACCI PATTERNS HELP PLANTS TO SURVIVE.

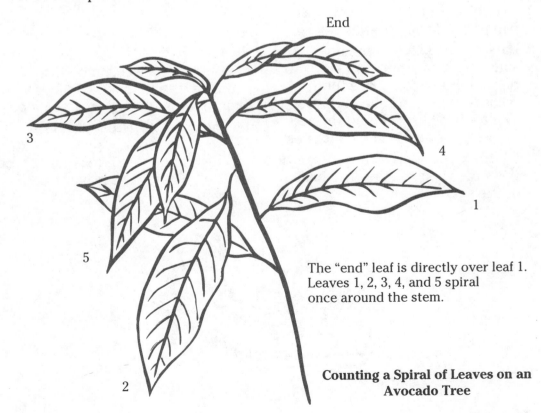

The "end" leaf is directly over leaf 1. Leaves 1, 2, 3, 4, and 5 spiral once around the stem.

Counting a Spiral of Leaves on an Avocado Tree

KEEP YOUR PLANT GROWING

After you have finished your measurements, keep your avocado. You won't get an avocado to eat, but you will have a pretty house plant.

Here's how to keep your avocado plant growing:

1. Don't pinch back or cut the plant until after you have finished your measurements. Then, whenever your plant seems to grow too tall and scraggly, pinch back the growing tip. Cutting back the plant helps it to grow thick and bushy.

2. Water the plant every couple of days.

3. When the plant is big enough, consider transplanting it into a larger pot.

YOU MAY EVEN WANT TO GIVE YOUR AVOCADO TO SOMEONE AS A GIFT YOU GREW YOURSELF.

. . . .

DO AN EXPERIMENT TO SEE HOW PLANTS SURVIVE

. . . .

Look carefully at the growth spirals on a pussywillow, on your avocado, or on another plant. You can see that the buds, twigs, or leaves grow at different angles.

You will probably see also that within each spiral no twig or leaf is directly over another twig or leaf.

You know that plants need light and moisture.

Try shining a light directly over the plant, and see whether it hits all the leaves. You may expect to see that no twig or leaf blocks out the light from the twig or leaf directly under it. The twigs and leaves in each spiral are growing at different angles, and these angles let in the sun.

Water the plant from directly above, and see whether the water hits all the twigs and leaves. If the twigs and leaves of each spiral grow at different angles, rain gets to all of them in almost equal amounts.

TWIGS AND LEAVES USUALLY GROW AT DIFFERENT ANGLES AND IN FIBONACCI PROPORTIONS. YOU'RE SEEING HOW NATURE'S MATH HELPS PLANTS AND TREES TO SURVIVE AND PROSPER.

ANSWERS FOR SECTION 4: FIND OUT NATURE'S SECRET SHAPES AND PATTERNS

Figure Out Very Beautiful Numbers:

Continue the Fibonacci series like this:
1, 1, 2, 3, 5, 8, 13, 21, 34, 55, 89, 144, 233, ...

5. Go for Golden Shapes and Patterns

*T*here's an old saying that gold is all around you. Perhaps you haven't been seeing it because this is not the precious metal gold. This is another kind of gold.

It's a golden pattern, a design that is repeated inside and out. You've seen this same golden pattern so many times that you almost can't see it at all. It's part of your world.

When you see a landscape painting, for instance, look at the place where the sky and the land meet. The artist probably did not locate the horizon right in the center of the painting because the painting wouldn't look right. The painting wouldn't look right, either, if the horizon were very close to the top or very close to the bottom.

The artist may have chosen the golden proportion.

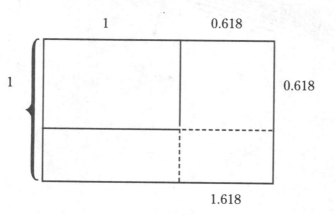

The Golden Proportion in Art

A proportion is the relationship of one part to another. In the golden proportion, one side of a rectangle is almost always longer than the other in nearly the same way.

Go on a search for the golden proportion. Once you know what to look for and where to look, you'll find it all over.

SOLVE A GOLDEN MYSTERY

Artists believe that people like to see the golden proportion in works of art. Try this experiment to see if you agree.

You are the director of a museum of art.

As guests enter the front door of the museum, the first work of art they see is a long table. Some 500 years ago, a great artist carved this table from rare and splendid wood.

Yesterday a modern artist finished a crystal vase full of glass flowers. The artist has donated this priceless work of art to your museum.

At last, you have the perfect object to place on the beautiful table. You want the vase to look just right. You want to place it in exactly the most artistic position.

Where will you put the vase? Will you put it directly in the center? Will you put it far to one side? Will you put it slightly to one side?

You can use both art and math to help decide.

. . . .

SOLVE A GOLDEN MYSTERY
continued

Here's what you need:

Plain paper or graph paper
A ruler
A pencil or pen
Scissors

Here's how to decide where to put the vase:

1. On the plain or graph paper, draw a line 8 inches (20 centimeters) long. That's your table top.

2. Now draw a vase with flowers about 2 inches (about 5 centimeters) high. Use the scissors to cut out the vase.

3. Now move your cutout around on the tabletop and see where the vase looks best.

YOU ARE USING MATH AND YOUR ARTISTIC EYE TO SOLVE A GOLDEN MYSTERY.

The Golden Proportion in Art
Where should the vase go?

· · · · · · · · · ·
TAKE A CHANCE ON THE GOLDEN PROPORTION

· ·

When you decided where to put the vase on the tabletop you just drew, you may have chosen the golden proportion or another sort of proportion.

How can you tell if you have found the golden proportion? You can tell just by looking. Or you can measure your tabletop and come up with a formula.

Use your calculator if you wish.

Here's how to find the formula for the golden proportion:

1. Place the vase cutout so that it is about 5 inches (12.5 centimeters) from one end of the table and 3 inches (7.5 centimeters) from the other end.

2. Now look for the golden proportion.

   As you have learned, proportion is a relationship of one part to another. The vase cutout divides the table into two parts. Divide one of these measurements into the other:

   For inches: 5/3 =
   For centimeters: 12.5/7.5 =

   You have the beginning of a formula that tells how the long part of the table relates to the short part.

3. Now find how the long section of the table relates to the whole length of the table. Divide the whole length, which is 8 inches (20 centimeters), by the length of the long section:

   For inches: 8/5 =
   For centimeters: 20/12.5 =

   You should get about the same answers for steps 2 and 3. (The numbers do not need to be exactly the same.) What you've found is that the long side of the table relates to the short side in about the same way that the long side of the table relates to the whole length.

   YOU'VE FOUND A FORMULA FOR THE GOLDEN PROPORTION.

DISCOVER THE FORMULA FOR GOLD

The ancient Greeks called this pattern you've been learning about the golden mean or golden proportion. They meant that this pattern is as precious as gold because it stands for balance and beauty.

The Greeks named the proportion for Phidias, the greatest of the ancient Greek sculptors. Then they shortened the name to one letter of the Greek alphabet, phi (Φ).

You may be interested to see the exact formula that mathematicians use for the golden proportion, or phi. Try it with your calculator.

The formula is $(1 + \sqrt{5})/2$.

Here are the keys to push on your calculator:

Push 1, then +, then 5 $\sqrt{}$, then =, then ÷, then 2, then =.

You should get the golden answer: 1.618034. You can go on and on with a long string of decimal places, or you can round the answer off to 1.6.

The rounded-off number gives you a good way to use the golden proportion in your own artwork:

If the small section is 1 part, the large section should be about 1.6.

Or turn the parts around: If the large section is 1 part, then the small section should be about 0.6

YOU CAN USE THE GOLDEN PROPORTION TO DRAW ALL SORTS OF SHAPES: RECTANGLES, OVALS, TRIANGLES, SPIRALS. YOU CAN FIND ALL THOSE GOLDEN SHAPES IN NATURE, EVERYWHERE YOU LOOK.

TAKE A GOLDEN MEASURE

Get out your calculator, and you can see how the golden proportion is related to Fibonacci numbers.

Here are the first 15 Fibonacci numbers:

1, 1, 2, 3, 5, 8, 13, 21, 34, 55, 89, 144, 233, 377, 610

Here's how to relate the Fibonacci numbers to the golden proportion:

1. Use your calculator to divide each Fibonacci number by the next higher number in the series.

   Remember that one way of stating the golden proportion is that, if the long side of a shape is 1, the short side is 0.618034. See how long it is before the numbers you divide come close to 0.618034.

   $1 \div 1 \quad =$
   $1 \div 2 \quad =$
   $2 \div 3 \quad =$
   $3 \div 5 \quad =$
   $5 \div 8 \quad =$
   $8 \div 13 \quad =$
   $13 \div 21 \quad =$
   $21 \div 34 \quad =$
   $34 \div 55 \quad =$
   $55 \div 89 \quad =$
   $89 \div 144 \quad =$
   $144 \div 233 \quad =$
   $233 \div 377 \quad =$
   $377 \div 610 \quad =$

2. Now turn the numbers around. Use your calculator to divide each Fibonacci number by the next lower number in the series. Remember that the other way of stating the golden proportion is that, if the short side of a shape is 1, then the long side is 1.618034. See how long it is before the numbers you divide come close to 1.618034.

   $1 \div 1 \quad =$
   $2 \div 1 \quad =$
   $3 \div 2 \quad =$
   $5 \div 3 \quad =$
   $8 \div 5 \quad =$
   $13 \div 8 \quad =$
   $21 \div 13 \quad =$
   $34 \div 21 \quad =$
   $55 \div 34 \quad =$
   $89 \div 55 \quad =$
   $144 \div 89 \quad =$
   $233 \div 144 =$
   $377 \div 233 =$
   $610 \div 377 =$

   Are you seeing a pattern?

THE HIGHER YOU GO IN THE FIBONACCI SERIES, THE CLOSER YOU GET TO THE GOLDEN PROPORTION. THE TWO IDEAS SHOW THE SAME BEAUTIFUL PROPORTIONS OF NATURE'S MATH.

FIND NATURE'S THREE-SIDED AND FOUR-SIDED SHAPES

You can see golden triangles in nature when you look at some trees or some types of flowers. If you want to see an especially beautiful golden triangle, look at an iris blossom.

You can find rectangles and other four-sided shapes in nature more often than you might think. Look around for evergreens and other trees that could fit inside a golden rectangle.

A Three-Petal Iris

Norway Spruce in a Golden Rectangle

GO ON TO SEE HOW TO FIND THE GOLDEN PROPORTIONS IN A LEAF.

············

MEASURE A LEAF

· ·

You may find the golden proportion in a leaf. You can probably find maple leaves outdoors or ivy leaves on an outdoor vine or on an indoor plant.

Here's what you do:

1. Smooth out the ivy or maple leaf onto a piece of graph paper or plain paper.
2. Use the ruler to draw a rectangle around the leaf. The four sides of the rectangle should touch the widest parts of the leaf.
3. Measure the long and short sides of the rectangle, or count the squares on the graph paper. Write the measurements as the ratio of the shorter side to the longer side of the rectangle. You may find a ratio something like 2/3 or 3/5.

YOU COULD BE SEEING A GOLDEN PROPORTION.

FIND NATURE'S FIVE-SIDED SHAPES

You can find five-sided shapes almost anywhere in nature. Pentagons and pentagrams are among nature's favorite shapes.

Here's where to look for pentagons:

• An apple or pear (Slice the fruit crosswise in half, and see the seeds at the core.)

• Other fruits and vegetables (Slice a zucchini just where the stem sprouts.)
• Starfish, sand dollars, and some seashells

• Many types of flower blossoms

MEASURE THE PENTAGONS AND PENTAGRAMS YOU FIND IN NATURE. YOU MAY DISCOVER A GOLDEN PROPORTION.

FIND NATURE'S SIX-SIDED SHAPES

Nature's six-sided shapes are sometimes hard to find, but not because they're not around. Rather, they're sometimes too small to see—and sometimes too big.

Big or little, six-sided shapes are found wherever nature needs to pack the most material into the least space.

Imagine the hexagons of a honeycomb inside a beehive. The bees need the most honey they can get into a very small space. The six sides mean no wasted space.

The six-sided shape can turn over and over without breaking or changing shape.

Here's where to look for hexagons:

- The bracts covering the rough outside of a pineapple
- A honeycomb (You don't need to disturb the bees. Some jars of honey are packed with a bit of honeycomb inside.)
- The kernels and the pattern on a cob of corn
- The back of a tortoise
- The cracking pattern in very dry ground

You can't see some hexagons without a magnifying glass or a microscope. A snowflake has six sides. These are fancy sides; snowflakes are not plain.

Ice crystals also have six sides, and they group in clusters, with six-sided figures on all sides. So do a few other molecules.

You may need a telescope to see some of nature's hexagons. A few years ago, astronomers discovered that a supernova had exploded far out in space. The gas bubbles that spewed out from the explosion clustered together in six-sided shapes. These giant shapes looked something like the tiny shapes of ice crystals.

YOU CAN FIND SIX-SIDED SHAPES THAT ARE UNIMAGINABLY LARGE, AND OTHER SIX-SIDED SHAPES THAT ARE UNIMAGINABLY SMALL.

FIND NATURE'S GOLDEN SPIRALS

You can find extraordinary spirals in nature.

Here are just a few of the most spectacular:

- The chambered nautilus. Its shell grows in a spiral so that as the creature inside grows, it always has larger and more comfortable housing.

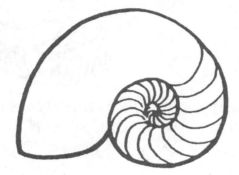

- The spiraling horns on mountain sheep, such as mouflons

- The spirals at the center of some tree trunks

· · · · · · · · · ·
FIND NATURE'S GOLDEN SPIRALS
continued

- Elephant tusks
- Some spider webs
- A cat's claws, if you forget to clip them
- A growing fern
- The spiral on the tail of a sea horse
- An ocean wave pounding
  toward the shore
- A hurricane or storm
  spiraling outward
- A galaxy of stars spiraling
  through the heavens

OLIVER WENDELL HOLMES COMPARED THE SPIRALS OF THE CHAMBERED NAUTILUS TO OUR HUMAN SOULS, WHICH, AS WE GROW OLDER, OUGHT TO GROW STRONGER AND WISER.

DESIGN TRIANGLES INSIDE TRIANGLES INSIDE TRIANGLES

A triangle can be golden. It's easy to construct golden triangles one after the other if you give the three sides measurements that are Fibonacci numbers.

Here's what you need:

Plain paper or construction paper
A pencil
A ruler
A drawing compass

Here's how to draw the triangles:

1. Construct a triangle. Make the base of the triangle 5 inches or 13 centimeters. Make the other two sides each 8 inches or 21 centimeters long. You have drawn an isosceles triangle, a triangle with two equal sides. Notice that all the measurements are Fibonacci numbers.

   Label the points of the triangle *A*, *B*, and *C*.

2. Place the compass point at *B*. Open it to the length of base *AB*.

Swing the compass in an arc, and make a mark where it crosses line *AC*. Label that point *D*. Draw a line from angle *B* to point *D*.

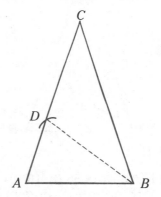

3. Place the compass point at *A*. Open it to point *D*. Swing an arc, and make a mark where it crosses line *BD*. Label that point *E*. Draw a line from *A* to *E*.

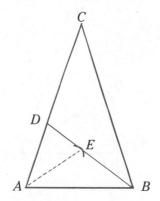

. . . .

DESIGN TRIANGLES INSIDE TRIANGLES
INSIDE TRIANGLES
continued

4. Place the compass point on *D*. Open it to point *E*. Swing an arc, and make a mark where it crosses line *AE*. Label that point *F*. Draw a line from *D* to *F*.

6. Place the compass point on *F*. Open it to point *G*. Swing an arc, and mark where it crosses line *EF*.

Label that point *H*. Draw a line from *G* to *H*.

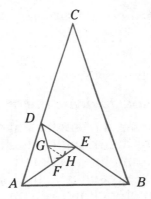

5. Place the compass point on *E*. Open it to point *F*. Swing an arc, and mark where it crosses line *DF*.

Label that point *G*. Draw a line from *E* to *G*.

7. Use your compass to draw a spiral from the golden triangles. Start at point *H*, and spiral in turn to *G*, *F*, *E*, *D*, *A*, *B*, and *C*. Open the compass wider as you move from point to point.

IF YOU HAD MICRO INSTRUMENTS, YOU COULD CONSTRUCT GOLDEN TRIANGLES FOREVER, EACH ONE SMALLER THAN THE LAST. OR YOU COULD CONSTRUCT LARGER AND LARGER TRIANGLES.

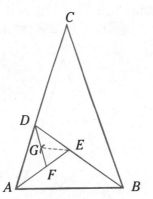

CUT A GOLDEN TRIANGLE

Just for fun, try measuring the base angle of any golden triangle. Then cut the base angle in half to form another triangle.

YOU'VE JUST CREATED TWO MORE GOLDEN TRIANGLES.

DESIGN FOUR-SIDED GOLD

You'll feel as if you're performing a magic trick. Begin with a square of any size, and end with a golden rectangle.

Here's what you need:

Plain paper or construction paper
A pencil
A ruler
A drawing compass

Here's how to design a golden rectangle:

1. Draw a square. The square can be any size that will fit on the paper with room to spare. Label the corners *A*, *B*, *C*, and *D*. Then extend the base line (*AB*) and the top line (*DC*) to about the length of the square (diagram 1).

2. Open the drawing compass to a little less than the length of a side of the square. Place the metal tip at point *A*, and swing an arc. Make one mark inside the square and a second mark below the square (diagram 2).

3. Place the metal tip of the compass on point *B*, and again swing an arc. Make marks that cross the other marks (diagram 3).

4. Line up the ruler where the arcs cross. Make a mark where the ruler crosses the base line. Label that point *E*. Make a mark where the ruler crosses the top line. Label that point *F* (diagram 4).

5. Place the compass tip at point *E*, and open the compass to the length of *EC*. Draw an arc from point *C* to the extended base line (*AB*). Label that point *G*. Keep the compass opening the same. Place the tip on point *F*. Draw an arc from point *B* to the extended top line (*CD*). Label that point *H* (diagram 5).

6. Draw a straight line from point *G* to point *H*. Now you have golden rectangle *AGHD* (diagram 6).

GO ON TO SEE HOW TO MAKE A GOLDEN RECTANGLE INTO A GOLDEN SPIRAL.

· · · · · · · · · · ·

DESIGN FOUR-SIDED GOLD

continued

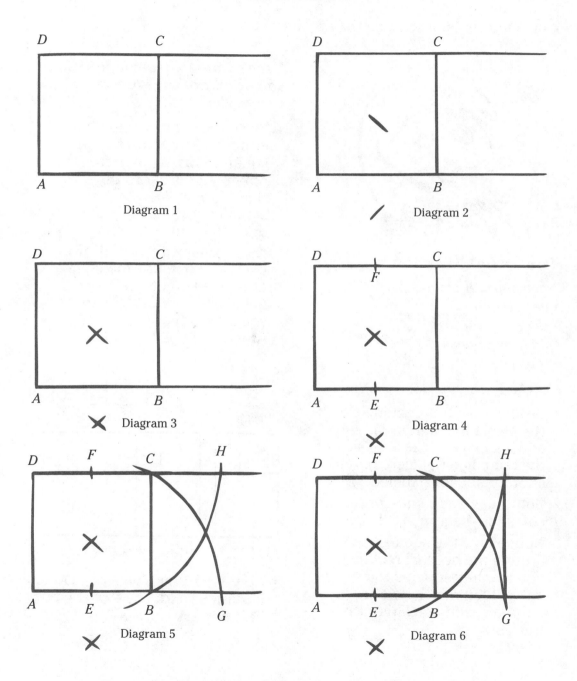

Diagram 1

Diagram 2

Diagram 3

Diagram 4

Diagram 5

Diagram 6

Designing a Golden Rectangle from a Square

CREATE A GOLDEN SPIRAL

You'll love golden spirals. They're fun to draw.

Here's what you need:

Graph paper or plain paper
A pencil
A ruler
A drawing compass
A triangle

Here's what you do:

1. Begin with a tiny rectangle (labeled 1 in diagram 1). Then add a square to the long side of the rectangle (labeled 2). Add another square (labeled 3).

2. Continue to add squares as shown in diagrams 2, 3, 4, and 5.

3. Notice how the squares spiral around the original rectangle. You're using squares to create one golden rectangle after another, each one larger than the last.

Here's how to draw a golden spiral within the golden rectangles:

1. Place the compass tip on the upper left corner of the smallest square. Draw a curve from the upper left corner to the lower right corner. If the first square is really tiny, you may have to draw that curve free hand.

2. Keep going with your drawing compass, opening the compass as needed. Keep the curve going from rectangle 1, to square 2, square 3, and all the way to square 8.

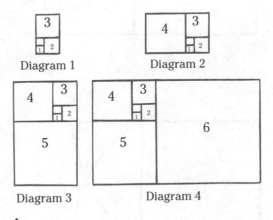

Diagram 1   Diagram 2

Diagram 3   Diagram 4

NOW THAT YOU HAVE YOUR OWN GOLDEN SPIRAL, YOU CAN USE IT TO CREATE A GOLDEN SPIRAL OF YOUR OWN.

CREATE A GOLDEN SPIRAL

continued

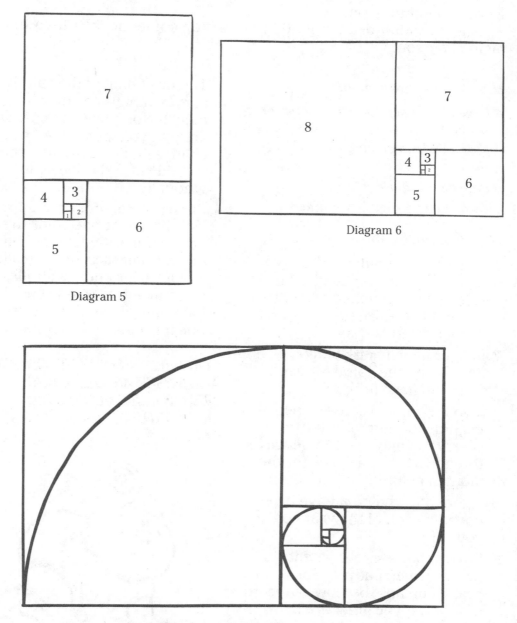

Diagram 5

Diagram 6

Creating a Golden Spiral

CREATE A GOLDEN LIFE SPIRAL

This is a way to map out your life. A golden spiral is a beautiful way to learn more about yourself.

You can also draw a golden spiral for someone you love or for a famous person.

Here's what you need:

A large sheet of construction paper or posterboard

A pencil with an eraser

A ruler

A drawing compass

Colored pens, pencils, or markers

Here's what to do:

1. Draw a large golden spiral by lightly drawing rectangles inside rectangles. (You might want to erase the lines after your spiral is completed.)

2. In light pencil mark off guidelines along the spiral for each year you have lived.

   If you wish, you can also pencil in guidelines for your future years. You may want to pencil in three-fourths of a space for the 9 months before you were born.

3. Figure out what you have been doing in each of the years of your life.

   If you wish, ask your parents to help you map out your early years. Perhaps they have a record of how fast you grew as a baby and how much you have changed.

The beginning of the spiral curves rapidly to show how quickly you grew and changed at first. As you grow older, you change more slowly, and the spiral widens and curves more gradually.

4. Choose colors for your spiral. You may want one color to show happy times, one for sad times, one for illnesses, one for school, one for trips and vacations, one for family events, one for special happenings, one for new friends, one for things you learned.

YOU WILL BECOME STRONGER AND WISER AS THE SPIRAL OF YOUR LIFE CURVES EVER OUTWARD.

. . . .

ANSWERS FOR SECTION 5: GO FOR GOLDEN SHAPES AND PATTERNS

. . . .

Take a Chance on the Golden Proportion:

Step 2.   For inches: 5/3 = 1.67
               For centimeters: 12.5/7.5 = 1.67
Step 3.   For inches: 8/5 = 1.60
               For centimeters: 20/12.5 = 1.60
These answers are all close to one another and to the value of phi, 1.618.

Take a Golden Measure:

These answers come closer and closer to the value of phi, 0.618034:

1 ÷ 1	= 1	21 ÷ 34	= 0.617647
1 ÷ 2	= 0.5	34 ÷ 55	= 0.618182
2 ÷ 3	= 0.666667	55 ÷ 89	= 0.617978
3 ÷ 5	= 0.6	89 ÷ 144	= 0.618055
5 ÷ 8	= 0.625	144 ÷ 233	= 0.618026
8 ÷ 13	= 0.615385	233 ÷ 377	= 0.618037
13 ÷ 21	= 0.619048	377 ÷ 610	= 0.618033

These answers come closer and closer to the other way of stating the value of phi, 1.618034:

1 ÷ 1	= 1	34 ÷ 21	= 1.619048
2 ÷ 1	= 2	55 ÷ 34	= 1.617640
3 ÷ 2	= 1.5	89 ÷ 55	= 1.618182
5 ÷ 3	= 1.666667	144 ÷ 89	= 1.617978
8 ÷ 5	= 1.6	233 ÷ 144	= 1.618056
13 ÷ 8	= 1.625	377 ÷ 233	= 1.618026
21 ÷ 13	= 1.615385	610 ÷ 377	= 1.618037

6. TRACE THE SHAPES AND PATTERNS OF YOUR OWN BODY

*P*hidias was the greatest sculptor of ancient Greece. His countrymen admired him so much that they named the golden proportion for him. Then they shortened the name to the first Greek letter of his name, phi.

Phidias was particularly interested in human proportions. Of course, he knew that people come in all sorts of sizes and shapes. His aim was to discover the perfect proportions.

The perfect human body, he decided, is $7^1/_2$ heads tall. In that body, he found the golden proportion. He also found golden proportions in the human face and hands.

Of course, Phidias was thinking primarily of sculptures of the human body rather than actual human beings. Yet the golden proportion is part of nature, and it is part of human beings, too.

You may find the golden proportion somewhere on your own body, and you may not. Whatever you discover, proportions are an interesting way to measure yourself—and other human beings.

TRACE THE SHAPES AND PATTERNS OF A GROWING BODY

During the Middle Ages (and even later in some places) in Europe, artists did not take into account the differences between children and adults. They tended to portray children as having the same proportions as adults.

Sometimes in early American paintings, too, you'll see children with adult proportions.

Look at the proportions of real children and real adults. You'll see that parts of the body grow at different rates.

Here's how to look at human proportions:

1. Look at the heads of babies, children, and adults in comparison to the size of their whole bodies. Look at the sizes of faces compared to the whole heads.

   The face of a child is small compared to the size of the head. But the child's head is large compared to the whole body.

   By the time you were 5 years old, your head had already reached over 90 percent of its growth. Your brain was already big and powerful. By the time a person is 15 years old, the head has nearly finished growing, perhaps more than 98 percent.

2. Look at legs in proportion to the rest of the body.

   The legs of a newborn baby make up about one-third of the baby's total length, and about 15 percent of total body weight. In an adult, the legs make up about one-half of the height, and about 30 percent of body weight.

Measure your own legs and see how long they are in comparison to the rest of your body.

3. Look at photographs of yourself when you were a baby, and see whether you can tell how your own proportions have changed.

   Usually, in the first year, the body grows rapidly, faster than the arms and legs. After that, the legs grow most rapidly.

TRACE THE SHAPES AND PATTERNS OF A GROWING BODY
continued

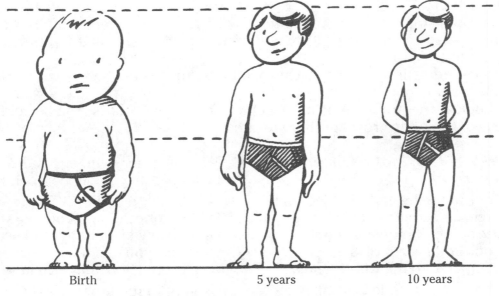

Birth   5 years   10 years

**Proportions of the Human Body from Birth to
Approximately 10 Years**

Between the ages of 10 and 15 years, there is another growth spurt. The feet and hands usually grow first (for a while, you may feel as though your feet and hands are too big for the rest of you). Then the legs and arms grow rapidly, then the body. Finally (though you won't be able to see this), the inner organs grow.

CAN YOU FIGURE OUT WHETHER PHIDIAS WAS RIGHT WHEN HE SAID THAT A PERFECT ADULT BODY OUGHT TO BE 7^1/2 HEADS TALL? PERHAPS YOU CAN FIND SOME KIND AND PATIENT ADULTS WHO WILL LET

YOU MEASURE THE LENGTHS OF THEIR HEADS AND THEN THEIR TOTAL HEIGHTS. IF THEY TURN OUT TO BE 7^1/2 HEADS TALL, YOU CAN TELL THEM THEY'RE PERFECT. THOUSANDS OF YEARS AGO, A FAMOUS MAN SAID SO.

FIND OUT WHAT SORT OF SHAPE YOU'RE IN

Imagine yourself inside a rectangle. What sort of rectangle would you make? Ask a friend to help you find out.

First, stand tall, and have your friend measure your height from head to toe. Then stand with your arms outstretched, and ask your friend to measure the distance from fingertip to fingertip.

Here are three possibilities:

1. You may be a tall rectangle. You are longer up and down than you are from fingertip to fingertip. You are longer vertically than you are horizontally.

2. You may be a perfect square. You measure the same distance both ways.

3. You may be a wide rectangle. You are longer from fingertip to fingertip than you are up and down. You are longer horizontally than you are vertically.

If you measure other people, both children and adults, perhaps you can see a pattern. You'll probably want to draw a chart like the one below to help you keep track of the number of people in each category.

NOW YOU CAN SEE WHETHER MOST PEOPLE ARE TALL RECTANGLES, SQUARES, OR WIDE RECTANGLES. YOU CAN TELL SOMETHING ABOUT HOW SHAPES AND PROPORTIONS CHANGE AS PEOPLE GROW UP.

	Adults	Older Kids	Younger Children
Tall Rectangles			
Perfect Squares			
Wide Rectangles			

FIND GOLD AT YOUR FINGERTIPS

Curl your forefinger, and look at the proportions of the figure formed. You may find a golden rectangle.

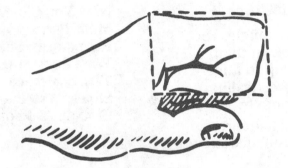

Gold at Your Fingertips

MEASURE THE PROPORTIONS OF YOUR OWN HAND

Just as you can find golden proportions in a seashell or a tree, you can sometimes find golden proportions in your own hand.

Since proportions change as people grow older, you may have to wait a while before your hand is golden.

You may also want to try measuring other hands.

Here's what you need:

Plain paper or graph paper
A pencil
A flashlight
A calculator

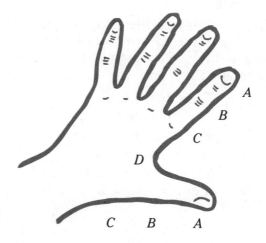

1. Trace your hand (or someone else's hand) on a piece of paper or graph paper. Sketch in the nails, joints, and knuckles.
2. Each of your fingers except the thumb has four bones in it from fingertip to wrist. Hold your hand over the flashlight. You may be able to see the bones and joints.
3. Choose any finger except the thumb. Start at the tip, and label the segments *A, B, C, D*. You can label the three segments of your thumb, too: *A, B,* and *C*.

Here's how to measure the proportions in a finger:

1. Measure each segment of the thumb and any other finger. You can measure in inches, centimeters, or squares on the graph paper.

Use the calculator to figure out the proportions for both the thumb and the other finger.

. . . .

MEASURE THE PROPORTIONS OF YOUR OWN HAND
continued

2. First, figure the proportion of *A* to *B*. Then figure the proportion of *B* to *A* + *B*.

$$A \div B =$$
$$B \div (A + B) =$$

The answers may be about the same.

3. Now find another proportion. Figure the proportion of *B* to *C*. Then figure the proportion of *C* to *B* + *C*.

$$B \div C =$$
$$C \div (B + C) =$$

You may find another answer that's about the same.

4. Figure the proportion of *B* to *C*. Then figure the proportion of *C* to *B* + *C*.

$$B \div C =$$
$$C \div (B + C) =$$

The answers might be about the same.

5. Now find yet another proportion for the finger that's not the thumb. Divide *C* by *D*.

$$C \div D =$$

Once again, the answer may be about the same.

What other Golden proportions can you find?

YOU'RE LEARNING HOW THE PARTS OF YOUR HAND GO TOGETHER. YOUR HAND MAY HAVE GOLDEN PROPORTIONS.

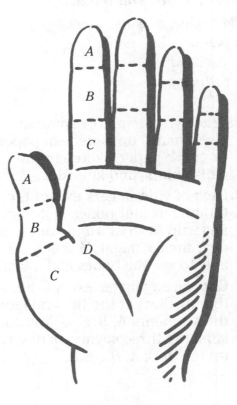

MEASURE THE PROPORTIONS OF A BEAUTIFUL FACE

You may find the golden proportions in a beautiful face. Then, again, you may not. Measure and find out.

For your model, find a close-up picture of a face, or look at a real face. If you're patient, you can look at your own face in a mirror. Or you can look at the face of a friend or relative.

Try making a sketch of the face you are studying. Even if you can't measure exactly, a sketch will help you see the proportions.

If you look carefully, you may be able to see three golden proportions in a human face.

Here's how:

1. Draw a rectangle around the face you have sketched. Label the right upper corner of the rectangle *A*, as in the diagram. Label the lower right corner *B*.

2. Draw a line across the center of the eyes. Label the right point of the intersection with the rectangle, *C*.

3. Draw a line across the nostrils. Label the right point of the intersection with the rectangle, *D*.

4. Draw a line across the face through the mouth. Label the intersection of that line *E*.

5. Look at the proportions.

   Compare distance *CD* and distance *DE*. You probably see a longer distance between lines *C* and *D* than between lines *D* and *E*.

   Then compare distance *CD* with distance *CE*. You may see a golden proportion.

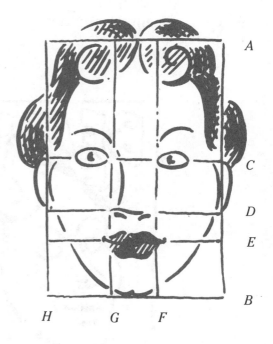

MEASURE THE PROPORTIONS OF A BEAUTIFUL FACE
continued

6. You can also draw two vertical lines down the face to intersect with the inner points of the eyes, the outer nostrils, and the outer edges of the mouth. Label as *F* and *G* the points of intersection with the bottom line of the rectangle. Label the lower left corner of the rectangle *H*.

7. Compare distance *BH* with *BG*, and *HB* with *HF*. You may or may not see another golden proportion.

EVEN WITHOUT EXACT MEASURING, YOU CAN FIND THE PROPORTIONS OF A HUMAN FACE. SOMETIMES THEY'RE GOLDEN.

TRACE YOUR OWN WHOLE BODY

Would you like to trace your whole body? You can find beautiful proportions. You need a friend to help. In fact, this is a good project for a group of friends. You may find that you and your friends all have different proportions, because you may be growing at different rates. Perhaps you can trace an adult, too, and see the different proportions of adults.

Here's how to trace your body:

1. Use freezer paper, brown wrapping paper, or other paper that comes in a long, wide roll. Roll out the paper to about the length of your body, and lie down on it.

2. Have your friend use a pencil to draw your outline on the paper.

Here's how to measure your paper self:

1. Use a yardstick to draw a rectangle around the outline of your whole body.

2. Mark the rectangle at these points:
   - The neck
   - The navel
   - The knees

Look for three proportions:

1. Look at distance A between the top of your head and your neck. Then look at distance B between your neck and your navel (diagram 1 on page 96).

   Compare A with B. Then compare B with the whole distance, A and B together ($A+B$).

2. Look at distance B' between your navel and your knees. Then look at distance A' between your knees and the bottoms of your feet (diagram 1).

   Compare A' with B'. Then compare B' with the whole distance, A' and B' together.

   The two proportions may be about the same.

3. Look at distance C between the top of your head and your navel. Then look at distance D between your navel and your feet (diagram 2).

TRACE YOUR OWN WHOLE BODY
continued

You might expect to see a shorter distance between the top of the head and the navel, and a longer distance between the navel and the feet.

Compare *C* with *D*. Then compare *D* with the whole length of your paper self, *C* and *D* together.

You may try comparing your own proportions with the proportions you find in your friends or in adults.

When you're finished, you may want to cut out your shape. You can draw and color over your paper self, and then put it up for display.

JUST FOR FUN, YOU COULD TRY THESE MEASUREMENTS ON A DOLL. MAYBE YOU CAN FIND OUT WHETHER DOLLMAKERS ARE FAMILIAR WITH THE GOLDEN PROPORTIONS.

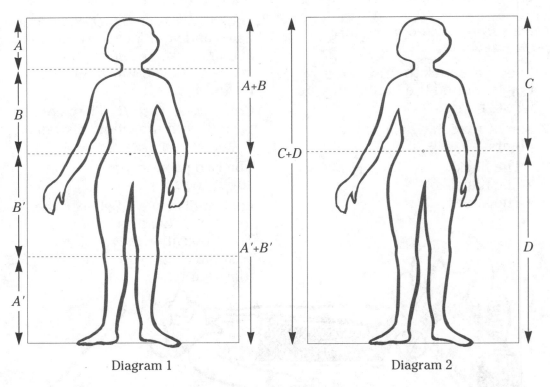

Diagram 1

Diagram 2

Finding the Proportions of Your Body

MAKE ANGELS

If you're lucky enough to have snow or sand to play in, try making angels. Just lie down, and move your arms up and down to make the wings. Then move your legs back and forth to make the robe.

SEE WHETHER YOU CAN GET OTHER PEOPLE TO MAKE ANGELS, TOO. THEN LOOK TO SEE ANGELIC PROPORTIONS.

MAKE A CHART FOR YOUR FRIENDS

You can do this project with a group of classmates or other friends.

Here's what you need:

A tape measure

A pencil or pen

Graph paper or plain paper

A calculator, if you wish

Here's what you do:

1. To begin the chart, list the names down one side. Across the top, list the types of measurements you'll make: height, head length, leg length.
2. Measure the height of each person in your group. Then measure the length of each person's head and the length of each person's legs.
3. Find the mean or average height. Add all the heights together, and then divide by the number of people whose heights you recorded. The result is the mean or average height.
4. Use the same method to find the mean or average head and leg lengths.
5. Now find the median height. List the heights in order from the shortest to the tallest. The median is the central number between the lowest and the highest numbers. (If you have an even number, the median is the middle two numbers.)

Here's how to find the median height in the sample chart:

$52^1/4$, 55, $55^1/4$, 56, $57^1/4$, $57^1/2$, $60^3/4$

For these seven people, the halfway number is 56. Half of the people in the group are shorter than 56 inches. Half are taller.

6. Look to see whether the mean or average is very much different from the median.

Name	Height (inches)	Head Length (inches)	Leg Length (inches)
John	56	$8^1/2$	$23^1/2$
Jeremy	$55^1/4$	$8^3/4$	$23^1/4$
Mary	$57^1/4$	$8^1/4$	$24^1/2$
Rowena	55	$8^1/4$	23
Ann	$60^3/4$	$8^5/8$	$25^1/2$
Beth	$57^1/2$	$8^3/8$	23
Wesley	$52^1/4$	$8^1/2$	22
Totals	392	$59^1/4$	$164^1/2$
Mean or Average	56	$8^1/2$	$23^1/2$

If the median is much lower than the average, that could show that someone is especially tall. If the median is much higher, that could show that someone is especially short.

For the heights in the sample chart, the mean or average and the median are the same. You

· · · · · · · · · · ·

MAKE A CHART FOR YOUR FRIENDS
continued

may see that your friends differ very much in height, even when they are about the same age.

7. Look at how long legs are in comparison to height. When your friends are fully grown, they will probably have legs about half as long as their adult heights.

8. Look at how long heads are in comparison to height. You recall that thousands of years ago the Greek sculptor Phidias said the perfect adult was $7^1/2$ heads tall. If your friends are not fully grown, they are probably not yet close to adult proportions.

You may find that the various lengths of their heads are not very different. That's true because the head grows first.

YOUR FRIENDS ARE ALL GROWING AT DIFFERENT RATES. IT'S INTERESTING THAT SOME PEOPLE WHO ARE SHORT NOW IN COMPARISON TO OTHERS MAY BE TALL IN COMPARISON LATER.

7. CREATE YOUR OWN SPECIAL DESIGNS

*W*ould you like to play with a puzzle you designed yourself?

Would you like to create holiday designs or your own snowflakes?

Would you like to see designs in words or in your own face?

Would you like to make a book of your own designs?

In this section you'll learn how.

MAKE A TANGRAM

With most puzzles, you can put the pieces together in only one right way. With a *tangram,* you can put the pieces together in hundreds of ways.

So far, people have invented more than 1600 tangram designs. There are whole books of these designs. There are even tangram jokes, silly designs that make people laugh.

The tangram idea comes from China. The first book to mention tangrams was published there in 1813, but the idea may be very much older. No one really knows. That's part of the mystery of the tangram.

Some people call all geometric-design puzzles tangrams, but there's only one kind of real tangram.

The seven pieces of a real tangram are called tans.

To make a tangram, use construction paper, posterboard, or other heavy paper. You may even want to cut out the tangram pieces in different colors.

Here's how to cut a square into the seven tans of a tangram:

1. Begin with a square.

2. Cut the square into two large triangles.

. . . .

MAKE A TANGRAM
continued

3. Fold one of these triangles along the dashed line as shown, and cut it along the fold.

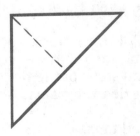

4. Fold the point of the other large triangle as shown and cut along the fold.

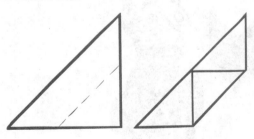

5. Fold the larger piece in half, and cut it into two pieces.

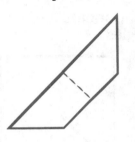

6. Fold one of the small pieces, and cut it along the dashed line as shown.

7. Fold the other small piece, and cut it as shown.

NOW THAT YOU HAVE ALL SEVEN TANS FOR YOUR TANGRAM, SEE IF YOU CAN PUT THEM TOGETHER TO FORM THE SQUARE YOU STARTED WITH. IT'S NOT AS EASY AS YOU MAY THINK.

PLAY WITH A TANGRAM

Were you able to put the square back together again? If you need help, here's how to do it:

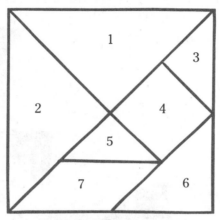

The Tangram Together

The seven pieces are numbered, so you can see where each one goes. Now see if you can make two cats. You must use all seven tans to make each cat.

Tangram Cats

If you feel creative, you can probably move your tans around to create other sorts of animals as well.

YOU CAN BUY BOOKS OF TANGRAM SILHOUETTES AND USE YOUR OWN TANS TO PUT TOGETHER THE DESIGNS. OR MAYBE YOU CAN FIND TANGRAM PUZZLE BOOKS IN THE LIBRARY.

CREATE YOUR OWN TANGRAM DESIGNS

You can create your own tangram designs, or you can put together designs that other people have invented.

The only rule is that you have to use all seven tans.

Here are some designs to try:

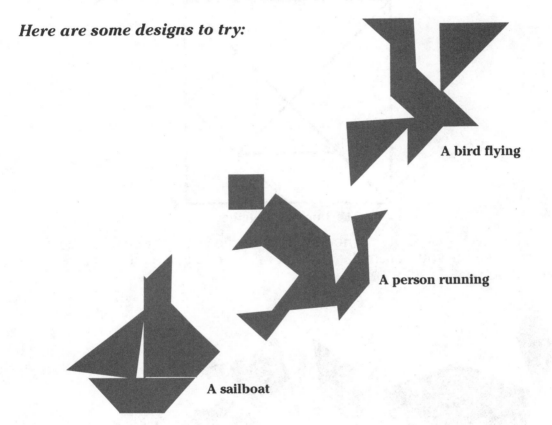

A bird flying

A person running

A sailboat

WHEN YOU PUZZLE OVER A TANGRAM, YOU HAVE SOMETHING IN COMMON WITH MANY FAMOUS PEOPLE. LEWIS CARROLL, THE AUTHOR OF ALICE IN WONDERLAND, LOVED TO PLAY WITH TANGRAMS. (HE WAS A PROFESSOR OF MATHEMATICS. HIS REAL NAME WAS CHARLES DODGSON.) AMERICAN MYSTERY WRITER EDGAR ALLAN POE ALSO LIKED TANGRAMS. SO DID THE FRENCH EMPEROR NAPOLEON BONA-PARTE AND A PRESIDENT OF THE UNITED STATES, JOHN QUINCY ADAMS.

A QUILT STORY

If you look at the designs and patterns of quilts, often you'll see a story.

Some quilts from the time of the War between the States tell the stories of battle.

A quilt can tell about family history, about marriages and births.

Other designs are traditional. Quiltmakers over the years have created traditional designs such as the Log Cabin, the Wedding Band, the Crown, the Star.

When you look at quilts, perhaps you can figure out how the stories and the designs go together.

YOU MIGHT LIKE TO CREATE DESIGNS AND STORIES FOR A QUILT OF YOUR OWN. GO ON TO CREATE YOUR OWN QUILT DESIGN BOOK.

A QUILT STORY
continued

Crown Quilt Pattern

The pattern can be changed in many ways. Use colors, textures, or patterns to create a design that pleases you. It would be fun to create a pillow using these patterns.

. . . .
MAKE A BOOK OF YOUR OWN DESIGNS
. . . .

This is your chance to be creative. Make a book of your own special designs.

Perhaps some day you can use your best designs to make a pillow cover or even a whole quilt.

Remember that your designs can tell a story, perhaps the history of your family, your town, or your own life.

Here's what you need:

Construction paper

Two-pronged paper fasteners

A pencil, drawing compass, protractor, triangle, and ruler

Scraps of paper and fabric

Scissors

Household glue

Crayons, coloring pens, or paints

Here's how to start a book of your own designs:

1. Decide on the size of book you want to create. For convenience, you may want to make your book the same size as a standard piece of paper, $8^1/2 \times 11$ inches (21.5×28 centimeters). Or you may want to make your book half that size.

2. Cut the construction paper into pieces the right size for the pages of your book. Hold the pages together with the two-pronged paper fasteners.

3. Decide on designs. To find interesting and beautiful designs, look at quilts and also at carpets, wallpaper borders, fabrics, and tiles.

4. Begin by drawing designs in pencil. Use the drawing compass, protractor, triangle, and ruler.

5. Then experiment with colors. Either glue scraps of colored paper and fabric on the parts of your designs, or use crayons, coloring pens, or paints to color the designs. See what looks good to you.

YOU CAN ADD DESIGNS TO YOUR BOOK WHENEVER YOU WISH. SAVE THE BEST DESIGNS FOR A MONTAGE, A WALL DISPLAY, A PILLOW COVER, OR A QUILT OF YOUR OWN.

MAKE A BOOK OF YOUR OWN DESIGNS
continued

An Amish Star Quilt Design

An Optical Illusion Design

This design changes as you look at it.

SOLVE A SYMMETRY PUZZLE

Look at a leaf or a butterfly. You could draw a line right down the middle. One half looks almost exactly like the other half.

In nature, things are often in balance. They have symmetry, that is, one part corresponds to another part.

Symmetry makes for beautiful and interesting designs.

Think of trees bordering a lake and reflected in it. There's symmetry in that reflection. In some designs, you can find more complicated symmetry and balance. Think of ripples in the lake that reflect the trees. There's a sort of balance, but not an exact symmetry in that reflection.

Here's a symmetry puzzle:

Draw a diameter straight through the center of a circle, dividing it in half. Each half looks like the other one.

You could divide a circle into four equal pieces, and all four parts would correspond. You could divide the circle into 16 equal pieces, and they would all look alike.

When would you have to stop? How many times could you divide the circle and come up with pieces that look alike?

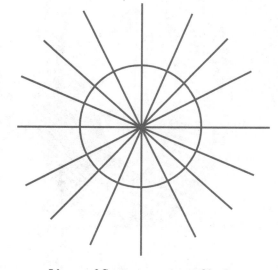

Lines of Symmetry on a Circle

THE ANSWER IS AN INFINITE NUMBER OF TIMES. YOU COULD DIVIDE A CIRCLE INTO ANY NUMBER OF LINES, NEVER STOPPING. THE PARTS OF THE CIRCLE WOULD ALWAYS BALANCE.

··········
SOLVE THE PUZZLE OF YOUR OWN FACE
·································

The human body has symmetry. If you drew a line up and down, you'd find a balance. Your body has two corresponding eyes, ears, arms, hands, legs, and feet.

People are complicated, though. The balance is not quite perfect.

Look at your own face in the mirror, or look at a very good photograph. Perhaps you'll see something different in each half of your face. It will probably be something small. You'll have to look closely.

Then think about how the image in the mirror is different from your actual face.

Hint: *Raise your right hand, and see which hand rises in the mirror.*

The opposite of symmetry is asymmetry.

YOU CAN PROBABLY THINK OF OTHER WAYS THAT THE HUMAN BODY IS NOT IN PERFECT SYMMETRY. LOOK AT YOUR HANDS AND FEET, FOR INSTANCE.

CHAIN TOGETHER HOLIDAY STARS

When you were in kindergarten, you probably made chains of people holding hands (and usually touching feet as well). Such a chain is a perfect example of symmetry.

   You can use the same idea for a holiday star design.

Here's how to make a star chain:

1. Fold a piece of paper in half lengthwise. Cut it in two along the fold.

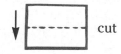

2. Fold one of the strips in half, then in half again and again. The more folds you make, the smaller your stars will be.

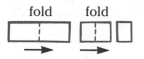

3. Draw half a star on top of the folded piece.

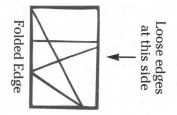

4. Cut out the star, but leave the points that touch the folds of the paper attached.

5. Unfold the paper, and you have a chain of stars. You can decorate, color, or add glitter as you wish.

   Would you like to use symmetry to cut out even fancier decorations?

. . . .

CHAIN TOGETHER HOLIDAY STARS
continued

Here's how to make designs that repeat in two directions:

1. After you fold the paper the first time, do not cut the paper in half lengthwise. Instead, fold the folded paper in half, then in half again and again.
2. Draw half of a star on the folded piece. This time, leave the top point of the star attached as well as the side point.
3. Open your paper, and see how many rows of symmetrical designs you have.

Hint: Whenever you design paper cutouts, keep the loose edges at the outside of the design. Make sure the points of attachment are on the folded edges only.

TRY A ROW OF FACES, FLOWERS, BUTTERFLIES, OR HEARTS. TRY EASTER BUNNIES, HANUKKAH CANDLES, HALLOWEEN CATS, SHAMROCKS, OR BIRTHDAY CAKES. CHAIN TOGETHER SPECIAL NUMBERS OR LETTERS, SUCH AS AN AGE OR A NAME FOR A BIRTHDAY PARTY.

··········
DESIGN SNOWFLAKES
· ·

A snowflake is one of the most interesting examples of symmetry and balance.

The symmetry of a snowflake has a lot in common with the symmetry of ice crystals, molecules so small that you would need an electron microscope to see them.

As far as anyone knows, no two snowflakes are alike. (Of course, nobody can know for sure.) Make paper snowflakes, and you'll probably find that no two come out exactly alike (unless you really work on making them the same).

Here's what you need:

Plain lightweight paper or circular filter paper

A drawing compass

A pencil

Scissors

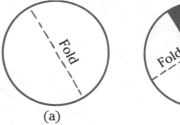

(a)

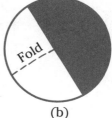

(b)

Here's how to make your own symmetrical snowflakes:

1. Use the drawing compass to draw a large circle on the paper. Cut out the circle. Or use a piece of circular filter paper.

2. Fold the circle in half as shown in (b). Fold it again as shown in (c). Fold it a third time as shown in (d).

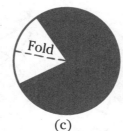

(c)

(d)

DESIGN SNOWFLAKES
continued

3. You can begin cutting designs now, or you can fold the circle one more time. Try both ways, and see what's different about the two kinds of snowflakes you make.

4. Cut small lacy designs along each fold. When you unfold the snowflake, you'll see the cut-out designs in symmetry.

NOW YOU CAN MAKE SNOWFLAKES FOR A MOBILE OR FOR WINTER HOLIDAY DESIGNS.

Note: Though *real* snowflakes *always* have only *six* sides, a *make-believe* snowflake is easier to make with *eight* sides.

CREATE WORDS UP AND DOWN, FORWARD AND BACKWARD

You may not think of words as symmetrical, but some have a kind of symmetry.

Write the word NOON in capital letters, and hold it up to a mirror:

It's almost the same up or down, backward or forward.

Think of other words that are spelled the same forward and backward. These words have their own kind of symmetry. Flip them backward, and they're still the same.

Think of three-letter family names: MOM, DAD, SIS.

Try spelling these names front to back and back to front: ANNA, BOB, LIL, ADA.

Words like these are called palindromes. There are even palindrome sentences.

Here are two famous palindrome riddles:

1. What did Adam say when he first met Eve?

    "Madam, I'm Adam."

2. What did Napoleon say after he lost his throne and was sent into exile on the island of Elba:

    "Able was I ere I saw Elba."

WHEN YOU'RE FEELING ESPECIALLY CREATIVE, THINK UP OTHER WORDS THAT YOU CAN SPELL THE SAME BACKWARD OR FORWARD.

RUN WITH SYMMETRY

Some time when you are running or riding a bicycle, think about symmetry. Your arms and legs are moving in rhythm. You need that rhythm and balance to run or ride. It's a kind of symmetry.

WATCH A DOG, A CAT, OR A HORSE RUN. LOOK AT THE LEFT FRONT LEG AND THE LEFT BACK LEG, THEN AT THE RIGHT FRONT LEG AND THE RIGHT BACK LEG. YOU'LL SEE A KIND OF SYMMETRY IN MOTION.

ANSWERS FOR SECTION 7: CREATE YOUR OWN SPECIAL DESIGNS

Play with a Tangram:

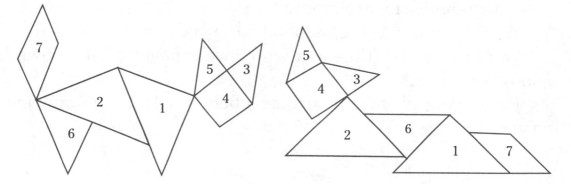

Create Your Own Tangram Designs:

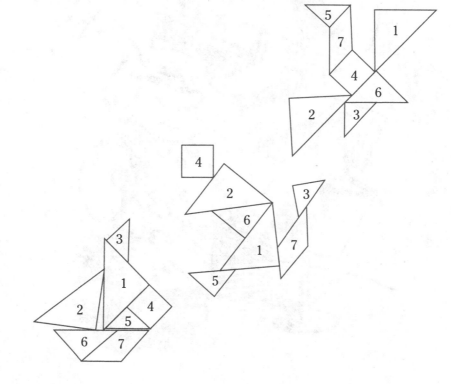

8. CREATE WORKS OF ART

Would you like to create your own three-dimensional shapes?

Would you like to float a mobile from a ceiling?

Would you like to design your own mosaic or your own good-luck puzzle?

Here's your chance to become a better artist in the wink of an eye.

....
CREATE ARTIST'S SHAPES
....

Some shapes fit together perfectly, with no wasted space. Other shapes are more complicated, and putting them together is a puzzle.

Either way, with simple or complicated shapes, you can create interesting designs. You'll want your shapes in as many colors and sizes as possible.

Here's what you need:

Construction paper in different colors
A pencil
A ruler, drawing compass, protractor, or triangle
Scissors
A small box

Here's how to make shapes to fit together:

1. Decide which shapes to construct. Assign one color for each set of shapes, for example, red for circles. Use the pencil and the ruler, drawing compass, protractor, or triangle to construct different shapes. You can draw them right up against one another on the construction paper so that you don't waste space.

   Draw many shapes and sizes, but be sure to have a dozen or so of each kind.

2. Cut the shapes out of the construction paper. To save time and work, hold several pieces of construction paper together, and cut out several shapes at the same time.

3. Keep your shapes in the box. Whenever you feel creative, you can add other shapes to the box.

Here are shapes you may want to construct:

- Squares
- Triangles—isosceles, equilateral, and other types
- Hexagons
- Parallelograms
- Arrowheads
- Circles
- Kites

CREATE ARTIST'S SHAPES
continued

Here are designs to try:

- A honeycomb of hexagons that fit together with no leftover space
- A design of equilateral triangles with no leftover space
- A grid of squares

- A design of hexagons, equilateral triangles, and squares with all figures touching and no leftover space
- A design of triangles fitted to form an octagon

GO ON TO USE YOUR SHAPES TO DESIGN MOSAICS, MONTAGES, AND FISH.

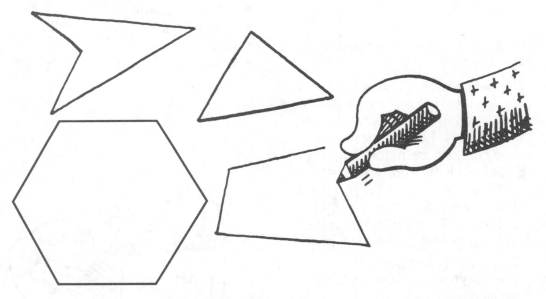

Shapes to Create Designs

DISCOVER AN ARTIST'S SECRET

Suppose you create a design out of only one regular shape. A regular shape is a shape in which all the sides are equal and all the angles are equal.

Identical copies of that one shape will fit together perfectly, with all figures touching and no leftover space.

Look for shapes that you can use for a design of this sort. You ought to find only three possible regular shapes. (If you can't find the three, or if you want to check your answer, see page 144 at the end of this section.)

YOU MAY DISCOVER A DESIGN SECRET.

....
DESIGN A MOSAIC
....

When you fit together shapes, you're creating a tesselation.

 You may have seen tesselations in mosaic flooring. An artist fits together tiny bits of colored stone, glass, or marble. (The word *tesselation* comes from a Latin word that means a small square stone.)

 Use your shapes to design a mosaic. This is a chance to be artistic. Try to put the shapes together so that they fit with no leftover space. You can fit them edge to edge. You can overlap them. You can combine colors.

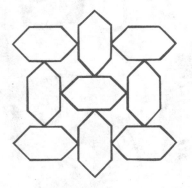

A Floor Tiling from the Taj Mahal

IF YOU WANT TO SAVE YOUR MOSAIC, PASTE IT ONTO A PIECE OF CON-STRUCTION PAPER OR POSTERBOARD.

MAKE A MONTAGE

A montage is a good way to display some of your favorite shapes and designs. To make a montage, you put together many designs and parts of designs to form a whole design.

Use shapes from your box to paste a design together on posterboard or on construction paper. Cover the whole area, with no background left showing.

You could try a large geometric design. You could try designs from a quilt. You could try letters of your own name or the words in a message.

Then decorate that large design with small designs and parts of designs. The small designs can overlap onto the large design in whatever way looks good to you. Glue on pieces of fabric, colored paper, photographs, or cutouts from magazines.

YOU CAN HANG YOUR MONTAGE ON A WALL OR BULLETIN BOARD.

DESIGN YOUR OWN FISH

You can fit your shapes together in abstract designs, or you can use them to create a picture.

Decide on a shape you like for fish scales, and fit them together. You can tesselate a parallelogram to form scales for the fish:

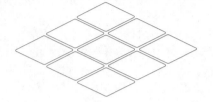

Then decide on shapes for the fins, tail, and other parts of your fish, and fit them together.

Choose the colors you want for the different parts, and color your fish.

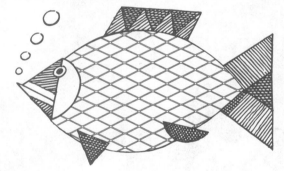

YOU MAY ALSO WANT TO CUT OUT SHAPES FOR SEASHELLS AND SEA PLANTS TO KEEP YOUR FISH COMPANY.

CREATE A DESIGN FOR YOUR MOTHER AND A FRIEND, A NO NO, AND A GOOD LAUGH

This is a good project for especially creative people. Create designs with letters of the alphabet.

Cut letters from construction paper. (You can keep the letters in your box along with your other shapes.)

Then see how you can put the letters together to make designs.

Here are four suggestions:

1. Design a card for your mother. Put together the letters M, O, and M, and turn them upside-down to get WOW.

2. Design a card for a friend. Fit the letters of your friend's name or initials together in odd shapes. Flip them around, or turn them inside out.

3. Put together N and O to create funny NO-NO designs.

4. Put together H and A for what looks like a lot of laughing.

YOU'LL ALWAYS HAVE A SPECIAL DESIGN FOR A HOLIDAY—OR MAYBE JUST FOR A JOKE.

. . . .

CREATE A DESIGN FOR YOUR MOTHER AND A FRIEND, A NO NO, AND A GOOD LAUGH
continued

Mom

No-no Designs

Hah

A Hill of H's

Creating Designs from Letters

DESIGN A GOOD LUCK PUZZLE

Some people think that ladybugs bring good luck.

Farmers think so because ladybugs eat lots of the insects that can destroy crops. Children sometimes think so because ladybugs seem so friendly. Pick one up, and it will contentedly walk back and forth from one of your hands to the other.

Here's a way to make a good luck puzzle of ladybugs. With this puzzle, you create a tesselation of ladybugs. Then you see who can put the ladybugs back together.

Of course, not all the beetles we call ladybugs are ladies. Half of them are male. But you already knew that, didn't you?

Here's what you need for your good luck puzzle:

Posterboard or construction paper
A pencil
A ruler
A triangle
Scratch paper
Coloring pens
Scissors ·

Here's how to design your puzzle:

1. On a piece of posterboard or construction paper, use a ruler and a triangle to block out a square.

   For a simple puzzle, construct a square with sides of 6 inches (15 or 16 centimeters). For a difficult puzzle, construct a square with sides of 9 inches (22 or 23 centimeters).

2. Divide the square into blocks of the same size.

   For the simple puzzle, divide the square into four blocks. For the difficult puzzle, divide the square into nine blocks.

   Each block ought to be 3 inches (7 or 8 centimeters) square.

3. On a piece of the scratch paper, draw some ladybugs. You need to design four different kinds, with different spots on their backs and different color combinations. Be sure to make all the ladybugs the same size.

· · · · · · · · · · ·
DESIGN A GOOD LUCK PUZZLE
continued

4. When you are happy with your four ladybug designs, cut them out and transfer them onto the puzzle. The front end of each ladybug should be in one block, with the back end in the next block.

Each block must have a front end or back end of each of the four ladybugs. You'll need to make some half-ladybugs to put around the edges of the blocks.

5. Color the ladybugs, and cut the blocks apart.

6. Scramble the blocks, and see who can put the ladybugs back together again.

: **YOU COULD MAKE OTHER PUZZLE**
: **TESSELATIONS OF PUPPIES, KITTENS,**
: **BIRDS, DRAGONS, DINOSAURS. YOU**
: **COULD TRY A PUZZLE THAT HAS**
: **FOUR DIFFERENT CREATURES.**

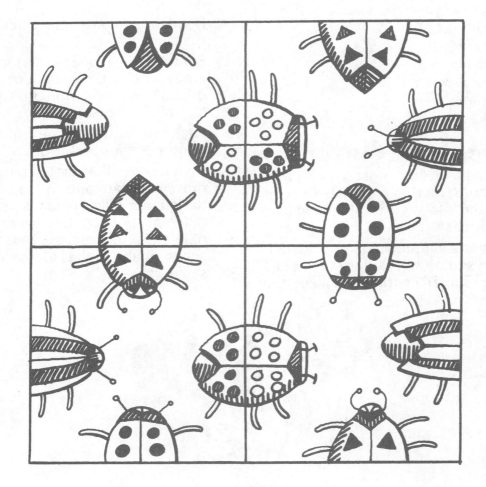

CREATE DESIGNS YOU CAN EAT

You can make tesselations with gelatin. Then you can eat them with your fingers.

Choose a different fruit juice for each color you want.

Here's what you need:

2 envelopes unflavored gelatin

2 cups fruit juice of the color you want

A small, heatproof glass bowl

A large spoon

An 8-inch (20-centimeter) square baking dish

A sharp knife

A spatula or wide knife

Use of a microwave oven and refrigerator

Here's how to make the gelatin:

1. In the glass bowl, sprinkle the unflavored gelatin over 1 cup (0.25 liter) of the fruit juice.

2. Heat in the microwave oven on high power for 2 or 3 minutes. The gelatin ought to dissolve, and the mixture should be just short of boiling.

   Caution: You need adult help with boiling liquid.

3. Stir in the other cup of fruit juice.

4. Pour into the baking dish.

5. Refrigerate until the gelatin has hardened.

Here's how to make gelatin designs:

1. With the sharp knife, cut the gelatin into shapes such as triangles, squares, or hexagons.

Caution: You may need adult help with cutting the shapes and getting them out of the pan.

2. Hold the pan in warm water for 10 seconds. Then carefully try to get the shapes out, using the spatula or wide knife. You may need to hold the pan in warm water for another 10 seconds.

3. Arrange the gelatin shapes on a plate.

   You can make designs with different gelatin shapes and colors.

SOMEONE (MAYBE YOU) IS BOUND TO EAT HOLES IN YOUR DESIGNS.

DRAW SHIFTING, TILTING DESIGNS

Tesselations are a good way to doodle. Try a row of stick figures. Try baseballs and bats. Try birds and wings. Try waves and curlicues.

Whatever they are, flip them. Turn them inside out. Draw shadows for them. Rotate them every way you can imagine. See how the shapes look at different angles.

A famous artist, M. C. Escher, drew tesselations where one form becomes another. Perhaps you've seen his designs of fish that become birds and birds that become fish. He did swans, flying horses, rows of men shaking hands, and whole books of designs. You'd like looking at them.

M. C. Escher Tessellation Designs

PERHAPS SOME DAY YOU'LL LOOK BACK AT A BOOK OF YOUR BEST DESIGNS. GO ON TO SEE HOW TO MAKE DESIGNS WITH THREAD.

MAKE DESIGNS WITH THREAD

Construct a figure with five, six, or eight sides, or even more. Then use it to create a colorful and beautiful design with thread.

You can frame these designs as gifts, or you can keep the designs for your own bedroom wall. You can display them on a bulletin board.

You can hang them on a mobile.

Here's what you need:

Scissors or a craft knife

A flat piece of plastic foam or foam-filled posterboard. (If you are making a mobile, use flat foam sheets or plastic foam left over from packing. If you are making a wall plaque, use foam-filled posterboard.)

A drawing compass

A protractor

A ruler or straightedge

Straight pins

Threads of various colors. (Use sewing threads or embroidery cotton, and if you wish, fluorescent colors.)

Laminating plastic. (You'll find sheets of laminating plastic at office or art supply stores or hobby shops.)

Here's how to create the thread design:

1. Use the scissors or craft knife to cut a rectangle from the plastic foam or foam-filled posterboard.

   > **Caution: You may need adult help in cutting with a craft knife.**

2. Use the drawing compass and the protractor to construct a circle and then a many-sided figure inside the circle. Decide how many sides you want: 5, 6,

8, or maybe 9, 10, or 12.

3. At each point (5th, 6th, 8th, or more) on the rim of the circle, carefully stick a pin in slantwise. The head of the pin must point outward.

4. Tie the end of a thread around one of the pins. Gently pull the thread around the outside of each pin all around the circle.

5. When you get back to the beginning, bring the thread in front of the second pin and then behind the third pin. Continue in that way around the circle again until you come back to the first pin.

· · · · · · · · · · ·
MAKE DESIGNS WITH THREAD
continued

6. Bring the thread in front of the second and third pins and then behind the fourth pin. Continue in that way around the circle again until you come back to the first pin.

7. Repeat the design until you have connected all the pins with thread. Tie the thread at the last pin.

8. If you are making a design to hang on the wall, measure, on the sheet of laminating plastic, a circle the same size as the circle of your design. Cut out the laminating plastic circle, and peel back the paper covering from the plastic. Carefully place the plastic over the thread design. Press it in place with your fingers.

9. Remove the pins.

If you prefer to make a see-through design for a mobile, see MAKE THREAD DESIGNS FOR A MOBILE, page 134.

YOU'RE READY TO FRAME OR MOUNT YOUR THREAD DESIGN WHEREVER YOU WISH.

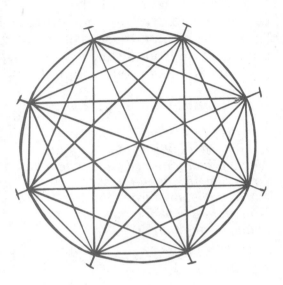

A String Design Created from an Octagon

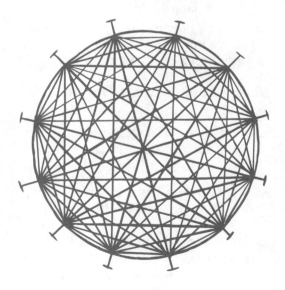

A Twelve-Sided Thread Design

MAKE EXTRA CREATIVE THREAD DESIGNS

You may want to put extra imagination and creativity into your thread designs.

Here's how:

1. Use two colors of thread at the same time.
2. Repeat the design with another color of thread.
3. Skip pins to make certain star shapes. (This is one way to make an octagon look especially interesting.)
4. Make a star design with one color of thread. Then continue connecting with another color.

DON'T STOP HERE. YOU CAN ALSO CREATE THREAD DESIGNS OF TRIANGLES, SQUARES, OR ANY OTHER GEOMETRIC FIGURES THAT STRIKE YOUR IMAGINATION. GO ON TO USE YOUR DESIGNS IN A THREE-DIMENSIONAL MOBILE.

· · · · · · · · · · ·
MAKE THREAD DESIGNS FOR A MOBILE
· ·

Imagine a gorgeous mobile floating from the ceiling over your bed. You can use thread designs to make the mobile. These are thread designs that you can see from both sides.

For a list of materials, look back at MAKE DESIGNS WITH THREAD, page 131.

Here's all you need to add:

A sheet of clear, flexible plastic of the type used for notebook dividers

Here's how:

1. Draw a circle on the clear plastic, and cut it out.

   To trace your circle on the plastic, you may want to use an awl, a darning needle, or the metal tip of the drawing compass.

   Another way is to make a paper pattern, and stick it to the plastic with a little rubber cement.

When you're finished, peel it off and remove the rubber cement by rolling it up with your fingers.

> *Caution: You may need adult help with rubber cement. Use it in a well-ventilated area.*

2. Place the clear plastic circle on a base made from the smooth plastic foam. Construct a many-sided figure inside the circle. You may want five, six, eight, or more points. Carefully stick in a pin at each point.

MAKE THREAD DESIGNS FOR A MOBILE
continued

3. Create the thread design. For help, look back at MAKE DESIGNS WITH THREAD, page 131.

4. Draw a circle the same size as the circle of your design on the sheet of laminating plastic. Cut out the circle, and peel off the paper backing. Carefully place the circle over your design. Press it in place with your fingers.

5. Make a hole near the edge of the design to insert the thread for hanging the design on the mobile.

6. Remove the pins. Pick up the clear plastic circle together with the laminating plastic circle. Set aside the plastic foam. (You can use the foam for making more designs.)

NOW YOU CAN SEE YOUR DESIGN FROM BOTH SIDES. YOU'LL WANT TO MAKE OTHER DESIGNS TO ADD TO YOUR MOBILE.

....
CREATE THREE-DIMENSIONAL DESIGNS
FOR A MOBILE

. . . .

You can also create three-dimensional (3-D) designs for your mobile. You can call these shapes by name:
- Tetrahedron for a figure with four sides
- Hexahedron for a figure with six sides
- Octahedron for a figure with eight sides

(Look for similar word forms—*tetra*, *hexa*, *octa*—in the names of two-dimensional figures, for example, tetragon, hexagon, and octagon.)

Notice that the models used to make these shapes are tesselations. A tesselation of four triangles makes a model for a tetrahedron. Six squares fitted together make a model for a hexahedron. A tesselation of eight triangles makes a model to create an octahedron.

Here's what you need:

Colored construction paper and/or sheets of colored flexible plastic of the type used for notebook dividers

A sharp pencil

A ruler or straightedge

A pointed instrument, such as a drawing compass, a punch, an awl, or a darning needle

Transparent tape or laminating plastic

Here's how to create a 3-D shape:

1. Look at diagrams 1, 2, and 3, on pages 138–139 and choose one to start with. With the sharp pencil, draw the basic design you want on a sheet of the construction paper or the colored plastic.

2. Fold so that *A* matches *A*, *B* matches *B*, *C* matches *C*, *D* matches *D* as in the diagram you are following.

If you are using construction paper, fold along a ruler or straightedge for a sharp, even fold.

If you are using colored plastic, use a pointed instrument to score the plastic and make it easier to fold.

· · · · · · · · · · ·
CREATE THREE-DIMENSIONAL DESIGNS
FOR A MOBILE
continued

3. Use a pointed instrument to make a hole to insert the thread for hanging the shape on your mobile.

> *Caution: You may need adult help with punching holes.*

4. Use transparent tape or laminating plastic to hold together the edges.

NOW YOU HAVE A THREE-DIMENSIONAL SHAPE TO ADD TO YOUR MOBILE. MAKE OTHER 3-D SHAPES, AND THEN GO ON TO SEE HOW TO PUT THE MOBILE TOGETHER.

CREATE THREE-DIMENSIONAL DESIGNS FOR A MOBILE

continued

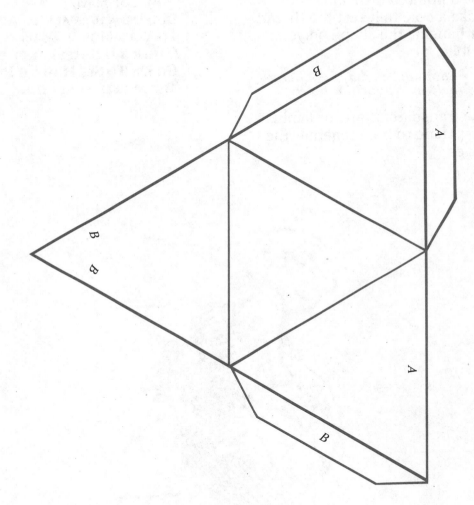

Diagram 1   Tetrahedron—four faces

CREATE THREE-DIMENSIONAL DESIGNS FOR A MOBILE
continued

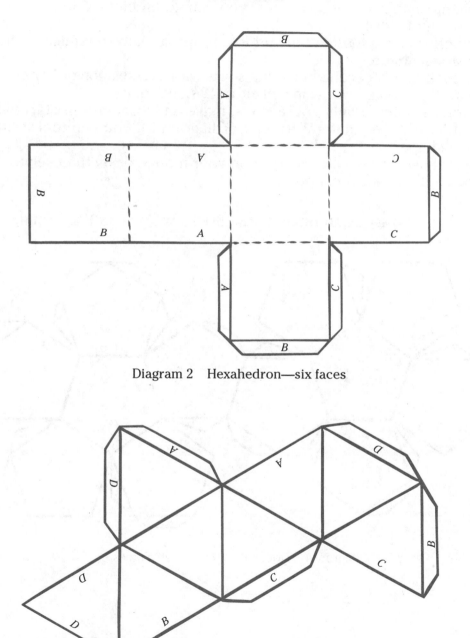

Diagram 2   Hexahedron—six faces

Diagram 3   Octahedron—eight faces

DESIGN SHAPES THAT FLY

In making shapes for your mobile, you can go on beyond four sides, six sides, or eight sides.

You can make a tesselation and fold it into a really complicated three-dimensional shape.

Try making a dodecahedron. That starts with a tesselation of 12 hexagons (diagram 1). You can fold the model into a 12-sided shape.

If you're feeling really courageous, make an icosahedron. Start with a tesselation of 20 equilateral triangles (diagram 2). You can fold it into a 20-sided shape.

Hang these complicated shapes on your mobile or by themselves. You can look at them with real pride.

TRY OTHER COMPLICATED DESIGNS, AND SEE HOW YOU CAN FOLD THEM.

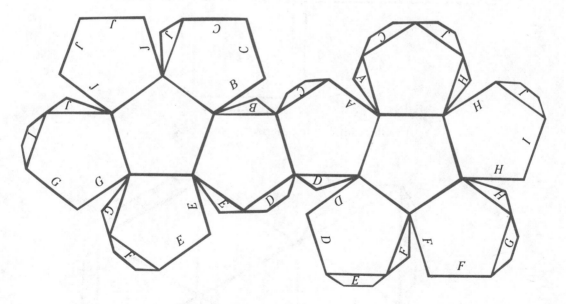

Diagram 1   Dodecahedron—twelve faces

DESIGN SHAPES THAT FLY
continued

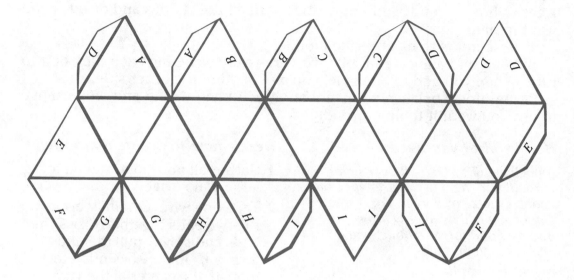

Diagram 2   Icosahedron—twenty faces

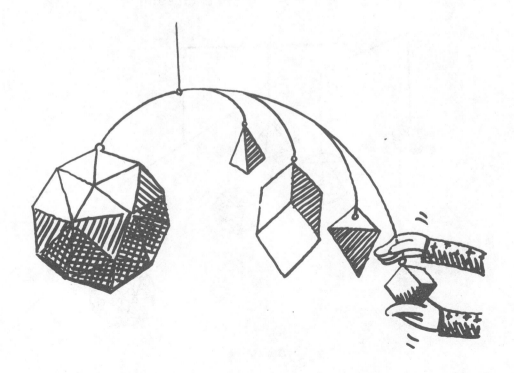

. . . .
FLOAT YOUR OWN MOBILE
. . . .

Here's how to put together a mobile with all the shapes and designs you want to hang on it.

The secret is to balance the mobile.

When you balance a mobile, you are really weighing each part of it in turn. When you add to one side, you must add to the other side.

If you don't balance your mobile, it will hang wrong and won't move freely. You want it to float proudly.

Here's what you need:

*A package of #18 wire flower stems
(You'll find them at department stores, hobby shops, or florists. For a small mobile, you'll need only three stems. For a larger mobile, you'll need seven or more.)*

Needle-nosed pliers

*Strong clear or black nylon thread or
black button thread*

Here's how to create a mobile:

1. Gather all your material on a large, flat surface.

2. Take one wire. Carefully bring the two ends together. Cross the ends and slowly pull them to form a $1/4$ inch (0.5 centimeter) loop in the center of the wire.

Make a similar loop in the center of each stem.

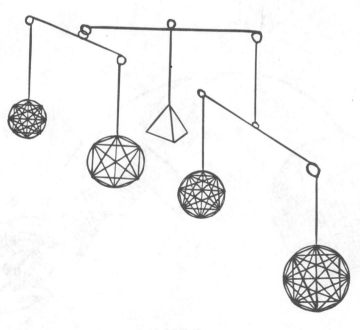

A Mobile

· · · · · · · · · · ·
FLOAT YOUR OWN MOBILE
continued

3. Use the pliers to make a small loop at each end of those stems.

4. Place one wire stem with the center loop facing away from you, on your work surface. Attach the center loops of two other wire stems to the loops at each end of the first wire stem.

> *Caution: You need adult help with using pliers.*

5. Instead of attaching another wire to one end of the stem you could tie a length of the strong black or clear nylon button thread. Each length of thread should measure 6 to 8 inches (15 to 20 centimeters) long. Then attach one of the wires to the thread. You can go on to make a large mobile by adding wires or thread to each end of the previous stem.

6. As you attach the wires, keep the mobile in balance. Each end of the wire must support the same number of additional wires. For example, if you attach a wire on one end, you must attach a wire on the other end.

7. Using thread, hang shapes and designs from the ends of each stem. You can also hang shapes from the centers of the stems, but you must always keep the mobile in balance.

8. Have an adult help you hang your mobile from a ceiling.

> **NOW YOU'VE BALANCED AND FLOATED A MOBILE. YOU MAY WANT TO MAKE OTHER MOBILES FOR HOLIDAY GIFTS.**

ANSWERS FOR SECTION 8: CREATE WORKS OF ART

Discover an Artist's Secret:

The only regular shapes that can fit together perfectly with no left-over space are squares, equilateral triangles, and hexagons.

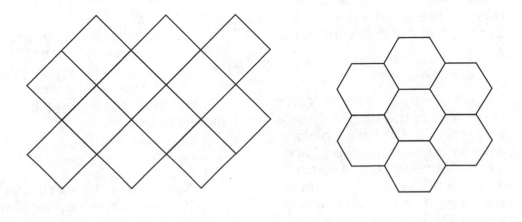

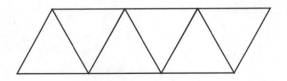

9. CREATE YOUR OWN RHYMES AND RHYTHMS

*I*f you're a math wizard, you probably like music. You like the beat, the rhythm, the harmony.

If you're a math wizard, you can double as a poet. You can write poems, and you can make up jokes, verses, and tongue twisters.

If you're a math wizard, you may take special pleasure in jumping rope and bouncing a ball. You can write your own nursery rhymes or rap songs. You can even design your own homemade instruments.

All those rhymes and rhythms fare better in the hands of a math wizard. A math wizard knows about the shapes and patterns, symmetry, balance, and beat of music and poetry.

Join the fun.

COUNT WITH RHYMES AND RHYTHMS

You can count without numbers. Count with rhymes and rhythms instead—just for fun.

Probably you already know the words to some familiar rhymes. Write them down. Then pick out the words or syllables with the strongest beat, and mark them with a downbeat sign (/).

Maybe you'll want to create your own counting rhyme.

Here's how to create a counting rhyme with a strong beat:

1. Repeat the same words over and over.

Miss Mary Mack, Mack, Mack,
All dressed in black, black, black,
With silver buttons, buttons, buttons,
All down her back, back, back.

This verse has 22 words.
Aren't the rhyming words more
fun than plain counting?

2. Use rhyme at the ends of lines. Maybe you want to finish with a surprise.

Eeny, meeny, pasadini,
Alla, bala, boomerini,
Archie, parchie, liverarchie,
And your brother George.

· · · · · · · · · · ·
COUNT WITH RHYMES AND RHYTHMS
continued

3. Use the same sounds over and over, especially at the beginning of words. (That's called alliteration.) Some counting rhymes use the same sounds so often that they almost become tongue twisters.

> A sailing sailor
> Went to sea
> To see what he could see, see, see
> But all that he could see, see, see
> Was the sea, the sea,
> The sea, sea, sea.

4. Keep a strong rhythm. This old-fashioned rhyme suggests a future occupation for yourself or a friend:

> Rich man, poor man, beggar man, thief,
> Lawyer, doctor, merchant, chief.

5. If you like, include a few numbers now and then, just for fun.

> One potato, two potato, three potato, four.
> Five potato, six potato, seven potato, more.

6. Put in your own name and the names of friends. Your counting rhyme can say something funny about your school, your games, and even about your own life.

THE WORDS OF A COUNTING RHYME DON'T USUALLY MAKE A LOT OF SENSE. A LITTLE NONSENSE IS PART OF THE FUN.

DRAW A PICTURE OF A POEM

You can see the shapes and patterns of a poem or a verse. Draw a picture to show them.

You might particularly like to draw a picture of a limerick that Edward Lear wrote:

> There was an old man with a beard,
> Who said, "It is just as I feared!
> Two owls and a hen,
> Two larks and a wren,
> Have all built their nests in my beard."

DRAW A PICTURE OF A POEM
continued

Here's how to draw a picture of a limerick:

1. Draw a grid with five rows of blocks. Rows 1, 2, and 5 are eight blocks long. Rows 3 and 4 have five blocks each. (The grid looks like a rectangle with a rectangular-shaped bite taken out.)

   You have a square for each word of the limerick. You're showing the length of each line.

2. When you pronounce the words of the limerick, check the emphasis. Then draw a special letter or shape, or just write the word BEAT in the square for each word that gets a strong beat.

   Hint: Lines 1, 2, and 5 have beats on three words each. Lines 3 and 4 have beats on two words each.

   You're showing the beat of the limerick. You're drawing a pattern.

3. Look at the rhymes. Draw a special letter or shape, or just write the word RHYME in the square for the first set of rhyming words. For two of the squares, you'll be drawing a second letter or shape for the second set of rhyming words. You may want to use different colors or two shapes that look good together.

   You're showing very strong emphasis on those words.

4. Look for symmetry and balance in the limerick. You're sure to see a pattern.

   A limerick is always five lines long. Lines 1, 2, and 5 should each have eight syllables. Lines 3 and 4 each have five syllables. Lines 1, 2, and 3 all rhyme. Lines 3 and 4 usually rhyme.

KEEP YOUR DRAWING. IT SHOWS YOU THE FORMULA FOR A LIMERICK. WHEN YOU WRITE A LIMERICK OF YOUR OWN, YOU'LL KNOW JUST HOW TO GO ABOUT IT.

\\\\	BEAT	\\\\	\\\\	BEAT	\\\\	\\\\	BEAT RHYME #1
\\\\	BEAT	\\\\	\\\\	BEAT	\\\\	\\\\	BEAT RHYME #1
\\\\	BEAT	\\\\	\\\\	BEAT RHYME #2			
\\\\	BEAT	\\\\	\\\\	BEAT RHYME #2			
\\\\	BEAT	\\\\	\\\\	BEAT	\\\\	\\\\	BEAT RHYME #1

USE SHAPES AND PATTERNS TO WRITE A HAIKU

Some poems make you think of drum beats or soldiers marching. If you put a poem like this into a shape, it would be something solid, such as a square or a triangle.

A Japanese haiku makes you think instead of a gently flowing stream or of waves breaking softly on a beach.

When you write a haiku, leave out rhymes. Don't count out any particular beat. Don't go out of your way to repeat words. Keep the rhythm subtle.

Concentrate instead on the image. A haiku is supposed to describe a single, simple image from nature.

You'll still see symmetry and balance.

· · · · · · · · · · ·

USE SHAPES AND PATTERNS TO WRITE A HAIKU

continued

Here's how to create the pattern for a haiku of your own:

1. Give line 1 five syllables.
2. Give line 2 seven syllables.
3. Give line 3 five syllables.

Here's a haiku about the difference between the light from a star in the sky and the light from a planet:

A planet sends light,
still, clear, without a twinkle.
Dancing is for stars.

THAT'S ALL. A HAIKU IS VERY SIMPLE.

COUNT ON A POEM

You may be surprised to hear that poets often talk about measures, just as math wizards do.

A poet may write by the metrical foot. That's a way to measure the rhythm of a poem. (For a poet, the word *metrical* has nothing to do with metric measurements.)

Try counting the metrical feet in your own favorite poem.

Here's how to count a poem:

1. Count the syllables in each line.

2. Mark the words or syllables with the strongest beat. Give each one a downbeat sign (/). Then mark each word or syllable that has a lighter beat with a curved sign (∪).

Hint: When you count a poem, look for one weak syllable, then one strong beat. That's iambic rhythm, one of the favorite rhythms of English-language poetry.

3. Count one metrical foot each time a pattern repeats in a line.

How many metrical feet are there in each line of Robert Frost's poem?

4. Count the rhymes in your favorite poem. You may find a pattern of rhymes, too.

What lines of each stanza rhyme in Robert Frost's poem?

SOON YOU'LL BE READY TO COUNT THE RHYMES AND RHYTHMS FOR A POEM OF YOUR OWN.

COUNT ON A POEM
continued

⏑   /   ⏑   / ⏑ / ⏑ /
Whose woods | these are | I think I know. |
⏑   /   ⏑   /   ⏑ /   ⏑   /
His house | is in | the vil- | lage though; |
⏑   /   ⏑   / ⏑   /   ⏑   /
He will | not see | me stop- | ping here |
⏑ /   ⏑   /   ⏑ / ⏑   /
To watch | his woods | fill up | with snow. |

My little horse must think it queer

To stop without a farmhouse near

Between the woods and frozen lake

The darkest evening of the year.

He gives his harness bells a shake

To ask if there is some mistake.

The only other sound's the sweep

Of easy wind and downy flake.

The woods are lovely, dark and deep.

But I have promises to keep,

And miles to go before I sleep,

And miles to go before I sleep.

Robert Frost, "Stopping by Woods on a Snowy Evening"

SOLVE A METRICAL MYSTERY

You know about figures like triangles, pentagons and pentagrams, octagons and octagrams. A poet has similar words for the number of metrical feet in verses.

Look at the words below. See whether you can tell from the word forms *di*, *tri*, and so on, how many metric feet are in verses with these names:

- Dimeter
- Trimeter
- Tetrameter
- Pentameter
- Octameter

YOU'RE ON YOUR WAY TO SOLVING A METRICAL MYSTERY

COUNT ON SOUNDS

One of the many reasons poets need to think like math wizards is that sometimes they want to make a verse or an entire song sound like something.

Here's how to count and notice sounds:

1. Count the beats of these two favorite old songs. You won't find it hard to pick out the sound-alikes:

> The wheels on the bus go round and round,
> Round and round, round and round.
> The wheels on the bus go round and round,
> All day long.

> Oranges and lemons,
> Say the bells of St. Clemons,
> I owe you five farthings,
> Say the bells of St. Martins,
> When will you pay me?
> Say the bells of Old Bailey,
> When I grow rich,
> Say the bells at Shoreditch.

. . . .
COUNT ON SOUNDS
continued

2. Look at the very heavy beats of the strange ending of this rhyme. You'll see how a rhythm can sound scary.

> Here comes the candle to light you to bed.
>
> Here comes a chopper to chop off your head.

(Perhaps the last lines are not as nasty as they seem. In the game that goes with the verse, a line of children pass under a bridge of hands. At the last word, the hands come down, and the child who is caught is out of the game.)

3. Notice the beats in Henry Wadsworth Longfellow's "The Midnight Ride of Paul Revere."

<pre>
  / ∪ ∪   /   ∪ ∪   / ∪   /
Lis- ten, my chil- dren, and you shall hear
  / ∪   ∪   /   ∪ ∪ / ∪   /
Of the mid- night ride of Paul Re- vere.
    /   ∪∪ / ∪ / ∪ /
Hard- ly a man is now a- live
    /   ∪   /   ∪   ∪   / ∪   / ∪   /
Who re- mem- bers that fate- ful day and year.
</pre>

You may hear something about that fateful night, a horse galloping.

PERHAPS YOU CAN WRITE A POEM OR A SONG THAT SOUNDS LIKE SOMETHING. MARK THE BEATS, AND KEEP A GOOD COUNT.

COUNT ON SOUNDS IN A JAZZ POEM

More than 60 years ago, Vachel Lindsay was writing poems that sounded like jazz. Some people said his poems were almost too jazzy and too different to be poetry. Certainly, the poems didn't suit everybody.

Now when we look back at Vachel Lindsay, we see him as one of the first rap artists.

How did he make his poems sound like jazz? You can find out by drawing the shape and pattern of one of his poems.

Here is a verse from Lindsay's "Santa Fe Trail" about the first automobiles. Try drawing it like a series of heartbeats, with upbeats for all the rhymes and repeating words.

> ...Hark to the calm-horn, balm-horn, psalm-horn.
> Hark to the faint-horn, quaint-horn, saint-horn...
> Hark to the pace-horn, chase-horn, race-horn.
> And the holy veil of the dawn has gone.
> Swiftly the brazen car comes on.
> It burns in the East as the sunrise burns.
> I see great flashes where the far trail turns.
> Its eyes are lamps like the eyes of dragons.
> It drinks gasoline from big red flagons.

PERHAPS YOU COULD WRITE THE SHAPES AND PATTERNS OF YOUR OWN FAVORITE MUSIC.

· · · · · · · · · ·
WRITE A RAP SONG
· ·

If you drew shapes and patterns for rap music, you might find yourself creating loops and curves.

At first, you might think you could predict exactly how a rap song is going. It seems like a straight line of rhythm.

Then there is a sudden dramatic break. The song goes into a loop. Perhaps the singer's voice drops in pitch. Perhaps the singer stops suddenly and begins with an entirely different rhythm.

Then the singer abruptly loops back to the first rhythm.

Here's how to go about creating a rap song:

1. Think of a dramatic subject. Rap singers often talk about the conditions in the world that make them angry.

2. Think about drum beats. Rap music needs a very strong beat.

3. Plan to repeat important words and phrases.

4. Plan to repeat sounds. You don't have to use rhyme, but you can if you wish. You may even want a rhyme in the middle of each line.

5. Go for a sudden break in your voice and rhythm. Think about the people listening to you, and take the break just when you want to capture their attention.

PERHAPS YOU COULD WRITE THE SHAPES AND PATTERNS OF YOUR OWN FAVORITE RAP SONG.

DANCE WITH SHAPES AND PATTERNS

Perhaps you would like to design a dance. Of course, a dance has shapes and patterns. A simple dance may just follow a back-and-forth pattern. Another dance may go in fancy loops and curls.

You decide the shapes and patterns for a dance you like.

That's how a choreographer works, graphing each move so that the dancer knows exactly what to do.

Here's how to draw the shapes and patterns for a dance:

1. Draw the dance steps in order. First, draw footprints to show the dancers how to move their feet. You'll need to show a footprint pattern.

   For example, a waltz has three steps. The dancers vary the pattern by moving in circles or by moving straight ahead. The basic three steps, though, remain the same.

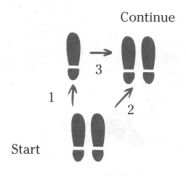

Diagram of Waltz Step

2. Think of a way to diagram how the rest of the dancer's body should move. A dance is far more than just footsteps.

For example, think of a diagram for the hokey pokey.

Here's how the dance goes: Put your right foot in, put your right foot out, put your right foot in and shake it all about. Do the hokey pokey as you turn yourself about, and that's what it's all about. Then you put in your left foot, your right hand, your left hand, your hip, your whole self.

The hokey pokey is a simple dance, but the diagram may not be simple.

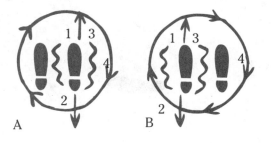

**The Hokey Pokey
(first two verses, A and B)**

3. Think of a way to draw the rhythm and speed of the dance.

   Perhaps you could use color for the footprints. Pink could mean slow, for instance, and bright red would be very fast.

DANCE WITH SHAPES AND PATTERNS
continued

The rhythm of the waltz might be slow and graceful throughout. The rhythm of the hokey pokey ought to get faster and faster and faster.

JUST LIKE OTHER ARTISTS, A DANCER OR A DANCE CHOREOGRAPHER NEEDS TO KNOW ABOUT SHAPES AND PATTERNS, DIAGRAMS AND GRAPHS.

PICTURE A TUNE

Here's another way to draw pictures of sounds: design a diagram or graph for music.

Your picture will not give you enough information to sing or play by. But it will give you an idea of how the sounds of music vary.

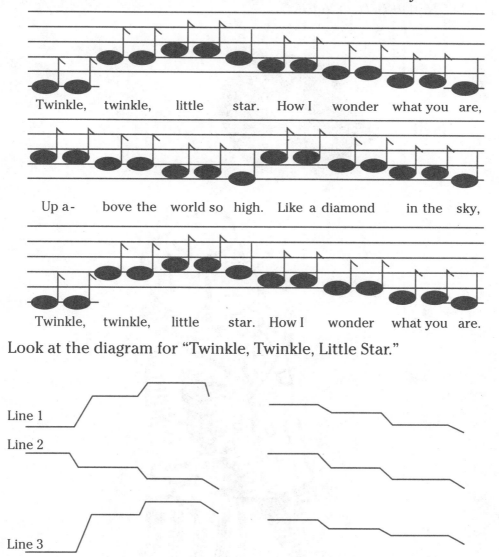

Twinkle,   twinkle,   little   star.   How I   wonder   what you   are,

Up a-   bove the   world so   high.   Like a diamond   in the   sky,

Twinkle,   twinkle,   little   star.   How I   wonder   what you   are.

Look at the diagram for "Twinkle, Twinkle, Little Star."

Line 1

Line 2

Line 3

Then draw a picture for a favorite tune of your own.

········

PICTURE A TUNE
continued

YOU MAY BE SURPRISED TO HEAR THAT ONE OF THE WORLD'S MOST FAMOUS COMPOSERS WROTE "TWINKLE, TWINKLE, LITTLE STAR." WOLF-GANG AMADEUS MOZART LIVED FROM JANUARY 27, 1756, UNTIL 1791. FIGURE OUT HIS AGE WHEN HE DIED, AND YOU'LL SEE WHY PEOPLE FEEL THAT HE DIED TOO YOUNG.

MAKE YOUR OWN TUNES AND RHYTHMS

You can design your own instruments. Then you can create your own down-home rhythm and harmony.

Here are four easy-to-create rhythm instruments:

1. Line up jars with a different amount of water in each. Strike the jars with a pencil or plastic pen, and you'll have your own musical tones.

   You'll need to experiment with how much water you need to make the right tones.

2. Hold the handles of two spoons in one hand with the curved bowls together. Then slap the spoons together and against your thighs. If you try hard, you may get good at it and be able to use more spoons.

3. Fill pop bottles with varying amounts of water. Blow across the tops of the bottles to make musical sounds.

4. Make a shaker by putting metal bottle caps into a small can or a plastic container.

YOU'RE ON YOUR WAY TO BECOMING YOUR OWN ONE-PERSON BAND.

MAKE YOUR OWN DRUM

You can practice making your own rhythms in whatever shapes and patterns you want. You can sing. You can clap your hands, slap your thighs, stamp your feet.

You can even make your own musical instrument.

Here's what you need to make your own drum:

A coffee can, large nut can, or plastic can

A sheet of heavy parchment paper

A pencil

A ruler

A drawing compass

Strong string

Scissors

A sink or pan of water

Paint, coloring markers, paper, cutouts for any decoration you wish

Here's how to make your own drum:

1. Put the can upside down on the parchment paper. With the pencil, trace the circle of the top of the can onto the paper.

2. Measure a circle about $1^1/2$ to 2 inches wider than the circle you traced. (That's 4 to 5 centimeters.) Use your drawing compass (or a pencil and string) to draw the wide circle. Then cut around the larger with the scissors.

3. Smooth out the parchment paper, and center it over the open end of the can. Tie the string tightly around the can to hold the paper in place.

Hint: You may want someone to help.

4. Dip the top of the can, including the string, into the water. Be sure to get both the string and the parchment paper wet.

5. Set your drum to dry. The parchment and string will shrink so that the drum surface is taut.

6. If you wish, decorate your drum. You may want to cover the drum with paper, and then decorate it with the paint or markers. Or you may want to paste on cutouts.

YOU CAN USE YOUR DRUM TO CREATE YOUR OWN RHYTHMS. PERHAPS YOU CAN DESIGN YOUR OWN BEATS AND RHYTHMS.

· · · · · · · · · · ·
MAKE YOUR OWN DRUM
continued

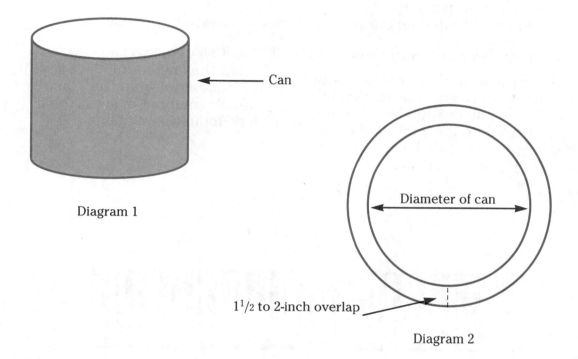

Can

Diagram 1

Diameter of can

1^1/$_2$ to 2-inch overlap

Diagram 2

Diagram 3

DISCOVER A MUSIC AND MATH SECRET

When you look at a poem or play a tune, look for Fibonacci numbers, such as 1, 2, 3, 5, 8, 13, or 21.

When you see how the numbers fit together, you may be looking at the golden proportion.

You may be finding out the proportions of beautiful sounds.

Here are places to start counting:

1. Look at a limerick or other poem. Count the metric feet in each line. Next count the number of lines. Then count the total number of metric feet in all the lines. Look for Fibonacci numbers.

2. Count an octave on a piano. Count the number of black keys, the number of white keys, and the total number of keys. You'll find Fibonacci numbers.

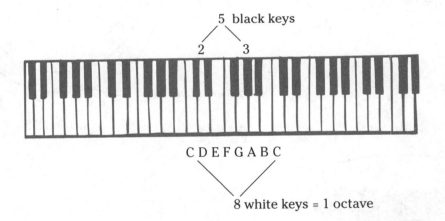

Piano Keys

DISCOVER A MUSIC AND MATH SECRET
continued

3. Count the number of notes in a scale: do, re, me, fa, sol, la, te, do. You'll find a Fibonacci number.

4. Play or sing a simple tune, like the ones below, and count the musical notes in each line.

Mary had a little lamb,
A little lamb, a little lamb.
Mary had a little lamb.
Its fleece was white as snow.

Are you sleeping, are you sleeping,
Brother John, Brother John?
Morning bells are ringing,
Morning bells are ringing,
Ding dong ding, ding dong ding.

Row, row, row your boat,
Gently down the stream.
Merrily, merrily, merrily, merrily,
Life is but a dream.

YOU'RE ON YOUR WAY TO BEAUTIFUL HARMONY. PERHAPS YOU CAN WRITE A TUNE FOR YOURSELF.

. . . .

ANSWERS FOR SECTION 9: CREATE YOUR OWN RHYMES AND RHYTHMS

. . . .

Count on a Poem:

Step 3: Count four metrical feet in each line of Robert Frost's "Stopping by Woods on a Snowy Evening."

Step 4: The rhymes repeat in lines 1, 2, and 4.

10. CRACK NUMBER CODES AND SEND SECRET MESSAGES

Would you like to design your own secret codes? Perhaps you'd like to design a device that lets you change your code with a flick of your wrist. You can write your diary in a different code every day.

You can send secret messages by using mysterious ancient numbers.

You can create special good-luck numbers or tell your fortune with mysterious numbers. You might even get a chance to outwit a movie producer or help with a famous escape.

WRITE A SECRET MESSAGE IN CODE

Suppose you want a secret code. Just turn letters into numbers.

Assign a number to each letter of the alphabet. Then you can write a secret message all in numbers.

Here's the code:

A = 1	J = 10	S = 19
B = 2	K = 11	T = 20
C = 3	L = 12	U = 21
D = 4	M = 13	V = 22
E = 5	N = 14	W = 23
F = 6	O = 15	X = 24
G = 7	P = 16	Y = 25
H = 8	Q = 17	Z = 26
I = 9	R = 18	

GO ON TO FIGURE OUT A SECRET ALPHABET MESSAGE.

· · · · · · · · · ·

DECODE A SECRET ALPHABET MESSAGE

· ·

9-13-1-7-9-14-1-20-9-15-14

9-19

13-15-18-5

9-13-16-15-18-20-1-14-20

20-8-1-14

11-14-15-23-12-5-4-7-5.

Hint: *This is a quotation from Albert Einstein.*

PERHAPS THIS CODE IS TOO SIMPLE FOR YOU. TOO MANY PEOPLE CAN FIGURE IT OUT. YOU MAY WANT TO SHIFT TO A MORE COMPLICATED CODE.

SILENTLY SHIFT AWAY FROM SIMPLE SECRETS

A code wheel makes coding so easy that you can use it to write a whole diary. You can even make a new code for each day of the week.

The idea is to shift up or down the alphabet. For instance, on one day match A with the number 5. On another day, match A with the number 21. As you change the number for A, all the other letters on the code wheel will automatically change to match with the proper numbers.

Here's what you need:

Construction paper, cardboard, or
  posterboard

A drawing compass

Scissors

A two-pronged paper fastener

A paper plate

A ruler

Pencils and pens

Here's how to make a code wheel:

1. On the construction paper, card-board, or posterboard, construct a large circle with the drawing compass. The circle should be 1 or 2 inches (3–5 centimeters) wider than the paper plate. with the scissors, make a

SILENTLY SHIFT AWAY FROM SIMPLE SECRETS
continued

hole in the center of the circle. This circle is the large wheel.

2. Use the two-pronged paper fastener to fasten the paper plate on top of the large wheel. The plate, which is the small wheel, ought to turn easily.

3. Use the ruler to divide the outer rim of the large wheel into 26 equal spaces. In each space, write a letter of the alphabet, from A to Z.

4. Use the ruler to divide the outer rim of the small wheel into 26 equal spaces. In each space, write a number, from 1 to 26.

5. To match a number with a letter of the alphabet, turn the small wheel. You can match any number with any letter, and you have an automatic code. For instance, put the number 23 at the letter N.

All the other numbers line up with letters, and you have another new code.

6. Think of other creative ways to shift an alphabet code. For instance, you could turn the alphabet backwards. Match Z to the number 1 and A to the number 26. Or you could skip some numbers and add others beyond 26. Or you might match the alphabet just to odd numbers or just to even numbers, adding numbers as needed.

GO ON TO TRY YOUR CODE WHEEL ON A SECRET MESSAGE.

DECODE A CODE WHEEL MESSAGE

12-26-23
5-7-11-12
5-19-25-1-21-19-4-4-17
5-19-25-1-21-19-4
7-24
19-6-17
5-19-25-1-21
11-9-13-19-10-23
23-14-23-10
5-19-22-23
20-17
19-6-17
5-19-25-1-21-1-19-6

Hint: *This is what Benjamin Franklin said about a magic square he especially liked. The first letter is T. Match that to the number 12 on your code wheel.*

USE YOUR IMAGINATION. YOU CAN SHIFT INTO AS MANY CODES AS YOU CAN DREAM UP.

· · · · · · · · · ·
CRACK AN ANCIENT EGYPTIAN NUMBER CODE
· ·

Most people won't try to figure out your secrets when they see them written in ancient Egyptian hieroglyphics.

The Egyptian numbers are easy to learn, though, because they make sense. They're fun to draw, too.

Before the ancient Egyptians learned writing, they probably counted with their fingers.

When they needed to leave a record of numbers for someone else to "read," perhaps the ancient Egyptians lined up leaves, pieces of rope, or flower blossoms.

Why do we think they did this? Later, when they developed a hieroglyphic writing system, they used drawings of leaves, pieces of rope, flowers, even snakes and tadpoles to indicate numbers.

1	)	(a papyrus leaf)
2	))	
3	)))	
4	))))	
5	)))))	
10	∧	(a bent leaf)
100	©	(a curled rope)
1,000		(a lotus flower)
10,000		(a snake)
100,000		(a tadpole)
1,000,000		(a surprised scribe)

Egyptian Hieroglyphics

The drawings were a sort of code for the real leaves and pieces of rope that they had used before. Perhaps they were counting cattle, farm crops, people, or days in a calendar.

CRACK AN ANCIENT EGYPTIAN NUMBER CODE
continued

Here's how to draw Egyptian numbers:

1. Begin by drawing a few sample number hieroglyphics.

2. Try the hieroglyphic for one million. It's a man (or a god) with a writing tablet in his lap. He's holding up his hands in surprise. He must think that one million is a suprisingly large number.

   The million hieroglyphic makes a good code for your name.

3. Try writing an actual number, such as your age or the year you were born, in hieroglyphics. Write it just as you write any number: left to right, from the largest place unit to the smallest place unit.

The Egyptians had no sign for zero, and they didn't think of it as a number. For example, the Egyptians wrote the number 20 as just two bent leaves.

4. Now think of a message that you want to put into code. Translate the letters in the words into numbers of our own alphabet. (If you need help, look back at WRITE A SECRET MESSAGE IN CODE, page 170.)

Then turn these numbers into Egyptian hieroglyphics. Will anyone ever crack that code?

DRAW THE HIEROGLYPHICS IN COLORS. YOU MAY FIND YOU HAVE A BEAUTIFUL AND ARTISTIC CODE. GO ON TO DECODE A SECRET EGYPTIAN MESSAGE

DECODE A MESSAGE JUST FOR YOU

A Message Just for You

Hint: *Translate the hieroglyphics into our numbers. Then look back at the alphabet code for WRITE A SECRET MESSAGE IN CODE (page 170), and translate the numbers into letters of the alphabet.*

GO ON TO TRY ANOTHER KIND OF ANCIENT CODE.

....

SEND ANCIENT GREEK MESSAGES

....

If we want to design an alphabet code, we must translate our letters into numbers. The letters of the ancient Greek alphabet, however, already were numbers. For instance, the second letter, beta, meant 2.

The Greek people used the connections they saw between words and numbers to try to understand the mysteries of the universe.

The first letter of the Greek alphabet, alpha, is still used to mean an important beginning. The last letter, omega, still means an important ending. The two letters together, alpha and omega, symbolize the ongoing cycle of life and death, beginnings and endings.

Look at the letters of the Greek alphabet, and you will see that most of them look like letters of our own alphabet.

1	A	(alpha)	60	Ξ	(xi)
2	B	(beta)	70	O	(omicron)
3	Γ	(gamma)	80	Π	(pi)
4	Δ	(delta)	90	Ϙ	(koppa, no longer used)
5	E	(epsilon)	100	P	(rho)
6	F	(vau, no longer used)	200	Σ	(sigma)
7	Z	(zeta)	300	T	(tau)
8	H	(eta)	400	Υ	(upsilon)
9	Θ	(theta)	500	Φ	(phi)
10	I	(iota)	600	X	(chi)
20	K	(kappa)	700	Ψ	(psi)
30	Λ	(lambda)	800	Ω	(omega)
40	M	(mu)	900	λ	(sampi, no longer used)
50	N	(nu)			

Greek Number/Letters

SEND ANCIENT GREEK MESSAGES
continued

Here's how to write ancient Greek number/letters:

1. Write them just as you write our own numbers: from left to right, from the largest place unit to the smallest place unit.

2. Try using Greek letters to write an important number such as your age or the number of people in your family.

YOU CAN USE GREEK LETTERS TO WRITE SECRET NUMBERS. PEOPLE WILL NEVER GUESS. THEY WILL THINK YOU ARE WRITING SECRET WORDS WHEN REALLY YOU ARE WRITING SECRET NUMBERS.

FIND A MYSTICAL, MAGICAL NAME

Notice that the numbers you write with Greek letters sometimes end up looking like a word, even if you don't quite know what the "word" means. Just for fun, use numbers to put together a strange new word of your own.

You could decide on a mysterious code name for yourself and your friends. You could find a good-luck name for a new pet.

This is not the way the Greeks developed their lucky names. This way is just for fun. You can even use your own alphabet.

Here's how to use numbers to form a name:

1. Write some important dates or other numbers.

   Suppose your pet was born on January 27 and came to live with you on April 3. Your own birthday is October 14. You can write those dates as 1–27, 4–3, and 10–14.

2. Translate these numbers into letters. (If you need help, look back at the alphabet code in WRITE A SECRET MESSAGE IN CODE, page 170.)

   For instance, 1–27 could become A-B-G. Then the date 4–3 becomes D-C, and the date 10–14 becomes J-N.

3. Move the letters around until you find a word that sounds like a good name. You don't have to use all the letters from the dates, and you can add letters if you wish.

   For instance, beginning with A-B-G, D-C, and J-N, You could come put with a name like DAN or JAN, JACK or DABBY, for a new pet. Your secret code name could be CADGE or GAB. Keep going until you find the one you like best.

GO ON TO USE NUMBERS AND LETTERS TO TELL A FORTUNE.

TELL A MYSTICAL, MAGICAL FORTUNE

The ancient Greeks used their number/letters to tell fortunes and to predict their luck. You could try telling your own fortune with numbers and letters.

This is not the way the Greeks did their predictions. This is just for fun.

Suppose you're planning a vacation. Perhaps you're leaving for camp or starting at a new school. Maybe you are playing in an important game, taking a test, or giving a party. You'll want to predict a lucky day.

Here's how to find a lucky day:

1. Write your own name and, under it, another important name.

   Suppose your name is Mary, and you want to visit Hawaii. Perhaps your name is Jeremy, and you play for the Red Sox.

2. Translate the letters in the names into numbers. (If you need help, look back at WRITE A SECRET MESSAGE IN CODE, page 170.)

For instance, the name MARY becomes the numbers 13-1-18-25. HAWAII becomes 8-1-23-1-9-9. JEREMY is 10-5-18-5-13-25. RED SOX is 18-5-4-19-15-24.

3. Match the numbers in each set of names.

13 1 18 25
8 1 23 1 9 9

10 5 18 5 13 25
18 5 4 19 15 24

. . . .

TELL A MYSTICAL, MAGICAL FORTUNE
continued

4. Try to find a lucky date.

Mary might like Hawaii best on the 13th day of the eighth month, August 13. Or maybe her lucky day is the first day of the first month, January 1.

Jeremy might pitch his best on the 18th day of the 10th month, October 18. Or perhaps he ought to try the fifth day of the fifth month, May 5.

You can find several other lucky days inside the number matches, too. It's a good thing this is just for fun. You might not know which day to pick.

SOMETIMES THE ANCIENT GREEKS FOUND THEIR NUMBER/LETTERS CONFUSING, ESPECIALLY FOR ADDING AND SUBTRACTING MANY NUMBERS. THE MYSTICAL MEANINGS WERE SO STRONG, THOUGH, THAT IF YOU HAD LIVED IN ANCIENT GREECE, YOU MIGHT NOT HAVE BEEN ALLOWED TO TRY ADDING AND SUBTRACTING. IN FACT, THE LAW FORBADE SOME KINDS OF PEOPLE TO LEARN ANY ARITHMETIC AT ALL.

SOLVE A MOVIE MYSTERY

Roman numerals are an ancient way to count, but you can still see them in use. The dates on old buildings and the hours on a clock are often given in Roman numerals. You might use Roman numerals to number the sections in an outline for a school paper.

Just as a movie begins, look for the date in Roman numerals. Here's the mystery: you may not have time to read the date. It flashes past at great speed.

Perhaps the producers don't want you to know how old the movie is.

1	I	8	VIII
2	II	9	IX
3	III	10	X
4	IV	50	L
5	V	100	C
6	VI	500	D
7	VII	1,000	M

Roman Numerals

Here's how to outwit the movie makers:

1. You should read just the last numerals. You already know that the first numerals stand for a year in this century, 19—.

2. Usually, you can just add up the last numerals. For instance, III means 1 + 1 + 1, our number 3.

3. Sometimes, though, you see a smaller numeral in front of a larger one. Then you have to subtract the smaller number from the larger number. For instance, IV means 5 minus 1, or our number 4.

Once you figure out how to read a date in Roman numerals, see if you can figure out how to write one. This is how a whole year looks in Roman numerals: MDCCLXXVI. (If you need help, look at SOLVE A REVOLUTIONARY MYSTERY, page 184.)

PERHAPS YOU CAN USE ROMAN NUMERALS TO WRITE A SECRET DATE. NOT EVERYONE CAN READ ROMAN NUMERALS AS FAST AS YOU CAN.

THE END

MDCCCCLVII

SOLVE A REVOLUTIONARY MYSTERY

Suppose you saw a date engraved in Roman numerals on a silver ink-stand: MDCCLXXVI.

Along with the date are mysterious initials: GW.

Who is GW? To find a clue, read the date.

Here's how to solve the mystery:

1. Add M + D + C + C. That's 1,000 + 500 + 100 + 100.

   That adds up to 17—, the first two numbers of the date.

2. Add L + X + X + V + I. That's 50 + 10 + 10 + 5 + 1.

That adds up to —76, the last two numbers of the date.

THE DATE IS 1776. COULD THOSE INITIALS BE GEORGE WASHINGTON'S?

THE STORY OF THE EMPEROR'S SECRET CODE

Nearly 200 years ago, Napoleon Bonaparte took over France and made himself the emperor. Napoleon loved war. He surrounded himself with vast armies that were able to conquer most of Europe.

Finally, the British defeated Napoleon and his armies. They sent Napoleon to live on the small island of Elba, off the coast of Italy.

Napoleon was not finished, though. He escaped from Elba and came back to fight again. He was ready for the greatest battle of all, the Battle of Waterloo.

As Napoleon approached Waterloo, his friends wanted him to surprise the British army. These allies sent a happy message to their supporters in the emperor's own code, the code he used only for his topmost secrets.

GO ON TO SEE THE MESSAGE THAT THE EMPEROR'S FRIENDS SENT, AND LEARN HOW TO DECODE IT.

DECODE THE EMPEROR'S MESSAGE

Here is the coded message Napoleon's friends sent:

TRLX HOEX ERFA EETB MPEL

Here's how to crack the emperor's code:

1. Look at the number of strange "words" in the message. Draw a grid with that number (five) of squares across.

2. Look at the number of letters in each "word." Draw your grid with that number (four) of squares up and down.

3. Put the words of the message into the grid, like this:

T	H	E	E	M
R	O	R	E	P
L	E	F	T	E
X	X	A	B	L

4. Form words from the message so it makes sense.

Hint: the original message from Napoleon's friends contained four words and a total of 18 letters. (That message was in French. This one is in English.)

THE MESSAGE WORKED. AS NAPOLEON MARCHED TOWARD WATERLOO, VAST ARMIES OF SUPPORTERS CAME OUT TO JOIN HIM. HE SURPRISED THE BRITISH, BUT IN THE END THE BRITISH WON. THIS TIME, THE BRITISH SENT NAPOLEON TO A MUCH SMALLER ISLAND WITH MANY MORE SOLDIERS TO GUARD HIM. NAPOLEON NEVER ESCAPED AGAIN.

SEND YOUR OWN EMPEROR'S MESSAGES

You can use the emperor's code for your own secret messages. It's one of the best.

Here's how to use the emperor's code:

1. Count the number of words and letters in the message you want to code.

2. Draw a grid. The number of words in your message tells you the number of up-and-down squares to draw.

3. Figure how many squares you need across the grid to get in all the letters of your message. Divide the number of letters in the message by the number of words. Then add a few squares so that your grid will be an even rectangle.

4. Write one letter of your message in each square of the grid. To made the code extra difficult, write every other line backwards. If you have extra blank

spaces left over, write an X in each one.

5. Read the squares of the grid from top to bottom. Write those groups of letters as your coded message. Write the letters in a line, not up and down. They'll look like strange "words" in a strange "sentence."

Hint: There should be the same number of letters in each of the strange "words" of your code.

⋮ YOU CAN THINK UP WAYS TO MAKE
⋮ THE EMPEROR'S CODE EVEN MORE
⋮ DIFFICULT. YOU DON'T ALWAYS HAVE
⋮ TO BEGIN THE MESSAGE AT THE
⋮ START OF THE GRID. YOU CAN
⋮ WRITE BACKWARDS. YOU CAN EVEN
⋮ SCRAMBLE THE LETTERS BEFORE YOU
⋮ PUT THEM ON THE GRID.

ANSWERS FOR SECTION 10: CRACK NUMBER CODES AND SEND SECRET MESSAGES

Decode a Secret Alphabet Message:

"Imagination is more important than knowledge."

Decode a Code Wheel Message:

"...the most magically magic of any magic square ever made by any magician."

Decode a Message Just for You:

Translate the hieroglyphics into numbers: 9 12-15-22-5 one million. Then translate the numbers into letters: I love [your own name].

Decode the Emperor's Message:

"THE EMPEROR LEFT ELBA."

11. COUNT OLD, COUNT NEW, COUNT ALL AROUND THE WORLD

*W*ould you like to count with your whole body? Would you like to grow a million flowers, pile up a million dollars, or—maybe not—do a million pages of homework? Would you care for a swim in money?

Would you like to stretch your imagination to the limit? Would you like to count how fast you're growing at this very minute—in atoms?

Here's your chance.

COUNT WITH YOUR FINGERS

Finger counting isn't just for babies.

A few very smart math wizards count with their fingers, even into the thousands. They can use their fingers almost like calculators.

All around the world, people have counted with their fingers so naturally that sometimes, as a language develops, the words for fingers also become the words for numbers.

That was true for a native American tribe with a beautiful name, the Dene-Dinje. They had an ancient and interesting method of quick finger counting.

Here's how to count with your fingers:

1. Begin with your fingers straight out. Then bend the little finger. That shows the Dene-Dinje word for the number 1: "The end is bent."

2. Now bend your ring finger. That's the word for the number 2: "The finger is bent once more."

3. Bend your middle finger. That's the number 3: "The middle is bent."

4. Bend your index finger (only your thumb is left straight). That's the number 4: "Only one remains."

5. Now bend your thumb. You're signalling the number 5: "My hand is finished."

OUR OWN NUMBER SYSTEM HAS A BASE OF 10. ONE OBVIOUS REASON IS THAT WE HAVE 10 FINGERS (AND 10 TOES, TOO), ALL AVAILABLE FOR COUNTING AND CALCULATING. NEVER BE ASHAMED TO USE YOUR FINGERS TO FIGURE OUT NUMBERS.

DANCE WITH NUMBERS

The people of New Guinea were famous for their complicated body counting. The most famous of all for body counting were the people of the Torres Straits, islands between New Guinea and Australia.

This way of counting is most fun if you bend and touch as fast as you can.

Here's how to body-count from 1 to 22:

1. The little finger on your right hand
2. Your right ring finger
3. Right middle finger
4. Right index finger
5. Right thumb
6. Right wrist
7. Right elbow
8. Right shoulder
9. Right ear
10. Right eye
11. Your nose

12. Your mouth
13. Left eye
14. Left ear
15. Left shoulder
16. Left elbow
17. Left wrist
18. Your left thumb
19. Left index finger
20. Left middle finger
21. Left ring finger
22. And your left little finger

HOW FAST CAN YOU COUNT?

········

MAKE NUMBER CARDS

· ·

If you like art, you'll like this project.

Use construction paper, cardboard, or posterboard to make number cards. You can use your cards to learn different kinds of numbers or numbers in a foreign language.

You might want to use colored paper with markers or coloring pens of different colors. You want your number cards to be as beautiful and colorful as you can make them.

Here's what you need:

Scissors

Construction paper, cardboard, or posterboard

A ruler

A pencil or pen

Markers or coloring pens

Here's how to make number cards:

1. With the ruler, draw 14 squares, each about 4 inches by 4 inches (about 10 centimeters by 10 centimeters) on the construction paper, cardboard, or posterboard. Use the scissors to cut out the squares.

2. With the pen or pencil, draw lines that divide each square into four equal parts.

3. Decorate and color one part of each square with one of our familiar Arabic numbers:

0 1 2 3 4 5 6 7 8 9 10 50 100 1,000

4. Decorate a second part of each square with the Roman numerals for the same number:

I II III IV V VI VII VIII IX X L C M

5. Decorate a third part of each square with the Chinese number.

MAKE NUMBER CARDS
continued

6. Decorate the fourth part of each square as if it were a domino, with dots for the number. Domino numbers go only up to 10, so you'll have to think of a creative way to express the numbers 50, 100, and 1,000.

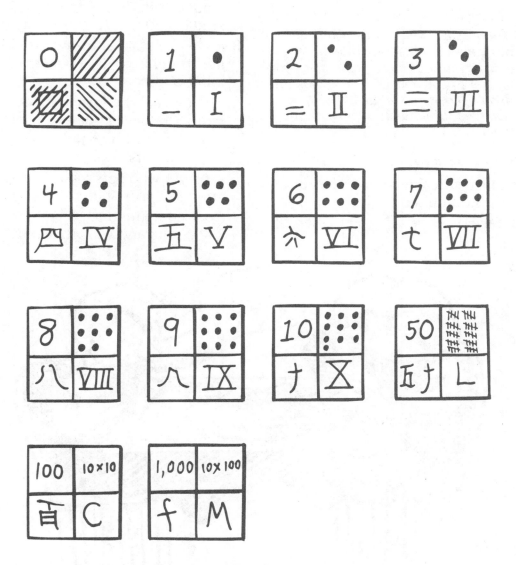

DESIGN YOUR OWN NUMBER CARD GAME

You can play games with your number cards. You can even design your own special card game.

Here's what you need:

A full set of number cards for each player

A set of "slush pile" cards (Don't decorate these cards. Just number them with as many of these numbers as you wish: 1 to 200 and 1,000 to 1,200. You don't need cards for all 400 of those numbers. Just make as many as you want.)

Here's how to play:

1. Make sure each player has a full set of number cards.
2. Take turns drawing a number from the slush pile. Place the number you draw face up, and read it aloud to the other players.
3. Have each player form that number from his or her own set of number cards.

   The player who forms the number first wins 10 points.

   The player who comes in second wins 5 points.

   A player who gets a number wrong loses 5 points.
4. Continue until one player has 100 points and wins the game.

DESIGN YOUR OWN NUMBER CARD GAME
continued

Here's how to design your own special game:

1. For your slush pile, make problem cards, for example, 34 + 16 or 12 × 8 or 90 − 25. You can make the problem cards as easy or as difficult as you wish.

2. If you wish, mix the problem cards with plain number cards. A player who draws a problem card uses his or her number cards to form the correct answer.

3. Instead, play the game backwards. Put down a number card. Each player must create a problem with that number as the answer.

For instance, if the answer number is 8, one player might put down 4 + 4. Another might put down 10 − 2. A third might put down 1 + 1 + 10 − 4. (Players must indicate whether they are adding or subtracting, multiplying or dividing.)

You might give points, not for the quickest answer, but for the longest answer.

YOU CAN MAKE UP YOUR OWN RULES FOR THE GAME. THIS IS YOUR CHANCE TO BE CREATIVE.

COUNT WITH OTHER COUNTRIES

You can make number cards for foreign languages, too. Put a numeral in one corner of each square. Then, in the other three corners, put the word for that number in three of these languages: French, Spanish, German, Japanese.

Or try out these number words with your friends.

Anywhere you go in the world, it helps to be able to count.

Here are foreign-language number words (and their pronunciations) for your cards:

Number	French	Spanish	German	Japanese
1	un	uno	ein	ichi
	(uhn)	(oo-noh)	(eye-n)	(echee)
2	deux	dos	zwei	ni
	(durh)	(dohs)	(z-vy)	(nee)
3	trois	tres	drei	sen
	(twah)	(trehs)	(dry)	(sĕn)
4	quatre	cuatro	vier	shi
	(kah-truh)	(kwah-troh)	(feer)	(she)
5	cinq	cinco	funf	go
	(sank)	(seen-koh)	(foonf)	(gō)
6	six	seis	sechs	roku
	(sees)	(says)	(sexts)	(rōku)
7	sept	siete	sieben	shichi
	(seht)	(s-yeh-tay)	(see-ben)	(shi-chee)
8	huit	ocho	acht	hachi
	(weet)	(oh-choh)	(ah-kt)	(hă-chee)
9	neuf	nueve	neun	ku
	(nuhf)	(nweh-bay)	(noin)	(kū)
10	dix	diez	zehn	ju
	(deess)	(dyess)	(ts-an)	(jū)

LOOK AT THE WORDS FOR NUMBERS IN THE THREE EUROPEAN LANGUAGES. YOU'LL SEE THAT THEY LOOK AND SOUND SOMEWHAT ALIKE. THE SIMILARITIES ARE EVIDENCE THAT THE WORDS FOR NUMBERS BEGAN IN THE SAME INDO-EUROPEAN TRADITION, A VERY LONG TIME AGO.

SPEND A DAY IN COUNTING SCHOOL

Suppose you had a teacher who really loved counting. The teacher tells you to start writing down numbers all day every school day.

You start writing 60 numbers per minute. That's one number per second, so you'd have to write fast. In fact, you'd shortly discover that nobody can write large numbers that fast. Let's pretend that you have lightning hands, high-speed automatic pencils, and an extremely long attention span.

Figure how long it would take to write one million (or one billion) numbers:

1. In the first hour, you start with the number 1 and write one number per second. You write 60 numbers per minute for 60 minutes.

   You'd get as high as $60 \times 60 = \square$.

2. Next, you write for a whole school day, 6 hours.

   Multiply the number you got for 1 hour times 6 hours = $\square$.

3. Then you write for a whole school week, Monday through Friday.

   Multiply the number you got for 1 school day times 5 = $\square$.

4. Next you need to find out how many school weeks it would take you to get to one million.

   Divide the number you reached for 1 week into 1,000,000.

5. What if you had to keep going to one billion? That's 1,000,000,000.

   To find out, multiply the number of school weeks you need for one million by 1,000. Then, if you want to know how many years that is, divide by 52, the number of weeks in 1 year. (That's a whole year with no vacations.)

PERHAPS YOU DON'T REALLY WANT TO COUNT THAT HIGH.

. . . .
DO A LOT OF HOMEWORK
. . . .

One million is a big number, hard to imagine. Imagine you had a million pages of homework to do. That's really an unhappy thought.

How far would the million pages stretch? Could you line the pages up across your school building? Across the whole town? All the way across the state?

Here's how to imagine that much homework (Use a calculator if you wish):

1. An ordinary sheet of notebook paper is 11 inches (28 centimeters) long. (Even if you usually use the metric system, you may find that your paper is measured in inches.)

   If you lined up a million pages of homework with no space between them, you'd need to multiply the measurement of one page by one million.

   In inches: $11 \times 1,000,000 =$

   In centimeters: $28 \times 1,000,000 =$

2. Now you need to convert the inches in your answer into feet, or the centimeters into meters.

   Total inches ÷ 12 inches per foot = ☐ (Round off the answer.)

   Total centimeters ÷ 100 = ☐.

3. The last step is to convert the feet into miles, or the meters into kilometers.

   Total feet ÷ 5,280 feet per mile = ☐.

   Total meters ÷ 1,000 = ☐.

. **NOW YOU HAVE AN IDEA OF HOW**
. **ONE MILLION PAGES OF HOMEWORK**
. **LINE UP. YOUR TEACHERS OUGHT TO**
. **BE IMPRESSED. GO ON TO SEE HOW**
. **MANY YEARS YOU'D NEED TO BE IN**
. **SCHOOL TO DO THAT MUCH HOME-**
. **WORK.**

. . . .

DO TOO MUCH HOMEWORK

. . . .

Now figure out how many years in school you would need to do a million pages of homework.

Here's how to figure the time:

1. Figure how long one page of homework takes you, on the average.

   Suppose you take 15 minutes to do one page of homework. That means you can do four pages in 1 hour.

2. Figure how many hours a week you do homework.

   For example, suppose you work 2 hours every school day, plus 3 hours over the weekend. That's $2 \times 5 + 3 = \square$.

3. Figure how many pages of homework you do in a week.

   For example, multiply the four pages of homework you can do in 1 hour by the number of hours you do homework in 1 week.

4. Find the number of weeks in your school year, minus vacations. Then figure how many pages of homework you could do in 1 school year.

   Many schools have a school year of 40 weeks. You could multiply 40 by the number of pages of homework you do in a week.

5. Find out how many years you'd need to do homework to get up to a million pages.

   Divide 1,000,000 by the number of pages of homework you do in 1 school year.

6. Maybe you need a whole class to help you do a million pages of homework. Divide the answer you got in step 5 by the number of people in your class. See if it helps any to share the job.

PERHAPS YOU'D BE JUST AS HAPPY WITHOUT QUITE SO MUCH HOMEWORK.

··········
PILE UP A MILLION DOLLARS
· ·

If you had a million dollars in one-dollar bills, could you keep the money in your pockets? Or would you need suitcases? Or maybe a large room?

How about ordinary paper grocery bags?

Here's how to guess how many grocery bags would hold a million dollars:

1. Guess how many crisp new one-dollar bills you could get into one large, strong grocery bag.

   Perhaps you could make piles of 100 bills each. Then possibly a big grocery bag might hold 100 of those piles.

Figure 100 dollar bills per pile × 100 piles = the total number of dollar bills you could get into one grocery bag.

2. Figure how many grocery bags you'd need to hold a million dollars.

   Divide 1,000,000 by the number of dollar bills you might get into one grocery bag.

THAT'S HOW MANY BIG, EXTRA-STRENGTH GROCERY BAGS YOU'D NEED TO CARRY A MILLION DOLLARS. NOW YOU KNOW WHY MILLIONAIRES PAY BY CHECK.

....
SWIM WITH THE MILLIONAIRES
....

What if you took an odd notion into your head: you want to swim in money. How much money would you need? Would a million dollars be enough?

You'll need to imagine a money-holding room inside your mansion. You'll need plenty of space to swim in sloppy, slippery money.

Here's how to figure out how many dollars you'd need for a swim (use a calculator if you wish):

1. Figure how many crisp new one-dollar bills you could pile into a stack 1 foot high.

   Suppose 100 dollar bills make a stack 1 inch high. That's 100 dollar bills per inch × 12 inches = □.

2. Figure how many piles you could get along two sides of a room about 8 feet × 8 feet square.

   Along one side of the room, put down the longer sides of the dollar bills. You can put down about two piles per foot times 8 feet. That's 2 × 8 = □.

   That's the number of piles you can put along one side of the room.

   Along another side of the room, put down the shorter sides of the dollar bills. You can put down about four piles per foot times 8 feet. That's 4 × 8 = □.

   That's the number of piles you can put along a second side of the room.

3. For the total number of piles your room could hold, multiply the number of piles for one side of the room by the number of piles for the second side.

4. Multiply the number of one-dollar bills in one 1-foot-high pile by the total number of piles your room can hold.

   That's the number of dollars you'd need to swim in money 1 foot deep. You really need a lot more money than that for a good sloppy swim.

5. To make the money 6 feet deep, multiply the number of dollars for a 1-foot swim by 6.

YOU COULD HARDLY SQUEEZE YOURSELF IN TO SWIM. YOU'D NEED A TRAP DOOR IN THE CEILING JUST TO GET INTO THE ROOM.

GROW A FARM OF FLOWERS

Perhaps you're not a greedy person. Maybe you don't dream of swimming in money. Perhaps you love nature instead.

Suppose your dream is to grow a garden with a million flowers. Your garden might stretch as far as you could see. It might cover a whole city.

To find out how a million flowers would look, you need to go outside and see how flowers grow.

Here's how to figure how much land you need to grow a million flowers (use a calculator if you wish):

1. Find a flower garden or a patch of wildflowers that you like. Measure 1 square foot or 1 square meter of the flowers.

2. Count the actual flowers inside the square. (If you count the flowers in other squares, you'll find more flowers in some, fewer flowers in others. So your count is an estimate of how many flow-ers might grow in an average square.)

3. Figure how many flowers would fit inside an acre or a hectare of land.

Multiply the number of flowers in 1 square foot by the number of square feet in an acre. Or multiply the number of flowers in 1 square meter by the number of square meters in an hectare.

Hint: *An acre is 43,560 square feet. A hectare is 10,000 square meters.*

. . . .

GROW A FARM OF FLOWERS
continued

4. Divide the number of flowers in 1 acre or 1 hectare into 1,000,000. Then you have the number of acres or hectares you need to grow a million flowers.

You may find you need a whole farm to grow a million flowers. Of course, in real life, you'd need a lot more space than just one huge garden. You'd need room to bring in water. You'd need paths for all the million people who would want to walk around and admire a million flowers.

MAYBE SOMEONE CAN SHOW YOU HOW MUCH LAND 1 ACRE OR 1 HECTARE IS ON A FARM, OR HOW MANY HOUSES OR BUILDINGS IN YOUR CITY SIT ON 1 ACRE OR 1 HECTARE.

......

GROW IN A ROW

....

If you grew a million flowers all clustered together on one big farm, perhaps not enough people could admire them.

Perhaps you want your million flowers all in a row, stretching far out into the world.

Here's another way to look at a million flowers (use a calculator if you wish):

1. Find a flower garden or a patch of wildflowers that you like. Measure a row of the flowers 1 foot or 1 meter long. Count the actual flowers in the row.
2. Figure how many of those flowers could grow in a row 1 mile or 1 kilometer long.

Multiply the number of flowers in the 1-foot row by the number of feet in 1 mile.

Hint: One mile is 5,280 feet.

Or multiply the number of flowers in a 1-meter row by the number of meters in a kilometer.

Hint: One kilometer is 1,000 meters.

3. Divide the number of flowers in 1 mile or 1 kilometer into 1,000,000.

Now you have an idea of how long a row of one million flowers ought to be.

Perhaps your row of flowers would stretch to another town or city.

NOW YOU NEED TO DECIDE HOW MANY KINDS OF FLOWERS YOU WANT TO GROW. IF YOU COULD TRAVEL ALL OVER THE WORLD, YOU COULD CHOOSE AMONG NEARLY A MILLION SPECIES, SUBSPECIES, AND OTHER VARIETIES OF FLOWERS.

WEIGH A MILLION

Here's one way to imagine a million. Figure out how much a million of something weighs.

Try this with different types of dry foods. You can weigh the foods, and then perhaps you can eat them.

This is a good project for a group.

Here's what you need:

Boxes of dry uncooked foods you can count, such as macaroni or spaghetti, dry cereal, peas, or rice
A food scale

Here's how to figure what a million weighs:

1. Take a sample of each type of dry food. With the scale, weigh a small portion of each, such as 1 ounce or a number of grams.

2. Count how many pieces or grains in the 1 ounce or in the number of grams you weighed.

3. Figure how many are in a whole box. Read on the side of the box how many ounces or grams the box holds. Multiply that number by the number of pieces or grains you counted.

   For example, suppose you counted 55 pieces of cereal in 1 ounce. The box holds 8.2 ounces of cereal. $55 \times 8.2 = 451$ pieces in the whole box.

4. Figure how many boxes you'd need to make a million pieces or grains.

In the example, divide a million by the total number of pieces in one box: $1,000,000 \div 451$ is about 2,217. To have a million pieces, you'd need 2,217 boxes of cereal.

5. To find what a million pieces weigh, multiply the weight of one box by the number of boxes needed to have a million pieces: 8.2 ounces $\times$ 2,217 = 18,187.6 ounces.

NOW YOU CAN FIGURE HOW LONG IT WOULD TAKE TO EAT THAT MUCH CEREAL. YOU MIGHT NEED SOMEONE TO HELP.

COUNT YOUR GOOD DEEDS

You might like to see how a hundred, a thousand, or even a million of something looks.

You might also like to do good deeds.

You might especially like to collect clothes for needy children.

Start a clothes collection at your school or club or in your neighborhood. This is a good project for a group of friends or club members.

Ask people to bring in old, clean clothes. You'll need a big box for the collection. You'll need a public place where people can easily drop off items.

Then donate the clothes to an organization that can distribute them to people who need them.

Here's how to plan ahead:

1. Estimate numbers. For instance, you'll want to think about the number of items that your big box can hold.

2. Estimate how much time you might need for the donations to fill the box. Perhaps you can deliver a full box once a month.

3. Keep a chart. Every time you see that your box is full and ready to deliver, mark the chart. Write the number of articles in the box and the length of time needed to collect them.

4. Mark categories on your chart. For instance, along with the total number collected, figure out useful ways to sort the clothes.

Here are some categories you might find useful:

- The number of items that need special sewing or repairs
- The number of items that people will need most, such as jackets and coats
- The number of clothes useful for winter wear. (Then you could subdivide that category into types such as jackets and mittens.)

COUNT YOUR GOOD DEEDS
continued

5. Think of a creative way to note the places on your chart where the categories overlap.

   You might find, for instance, a good winter jacket that needs buttons sewed on it. It belongs in three categories: special repairs, most needed, and winter wear.

6. Have a goal. Perhaps you want to collect 100 or 500 items. Perhaps your ultimate goal is 1,000.

Keep another chart that shows how far you are on your way to the goal.

ESTIMATE HOW MANY TIMES YOU'LL NEED TO FILL THE BIG BOX BEFORE YOU REACH YOUR GOAL. PERHAPS YOU'LL COUNT A VERY HIGH NUMBER OF GOOD DEEDS.

SOLVE A PRIME MYSTERY

Draw a picture that solves a mystery.

Here's the mystery: What is a prime number? This isn't an easy mystery. Supercomputers work on finding more and more prime numbers.

A math whiz can tell you the definition of a prime number. A prime number is a number greater than 1 that can be divided evenly by only two whole numbers, the number 1 and the number itself.

You can do a lot of dividing to find prime numbers, or you can draw pictures.

Here's how to draw pictures that solve the mystery of prime numbers:

1. Use graph paper or plain paper. Pick a number you like. Picture that number as a lineup of small squares. For instance, picture the number 3 as a lineup of three small squares. Picture the number 6 as a lineup of six small squares.

2. Then see how many ways you can arrange and rearrange the small squares. There is only one rule:

   If the small squares can make a rectangle only if they are in a straight line, you have discovered a prime number.

   If the small squares can be arranged into larger squares or other rectangles, you do not have a prime number.

3. Decide about 3 and 6, and then try a few more numbers. You can look at the diagrams to find some prime numbers and numbers that are not prime. Then draw a few diagrams of your own.

You ought to find a total of seven prime numbers before you reach the number 20. (Remember that the number 1 does not count.)

4. Don't look for a regular pattern of prime numbers. Prime numbers do not occur in a pattern that you can predict ahead of time.

There are an infinite number of prime numbers, just as there are an infinite number of numbers divisible by 2, an infinite number divisible by 3, and so on.

As the numbers get bigger and bigger, though, only a computer has the time and patience to search for them. A human being could take a lifetime to do all those calculations.

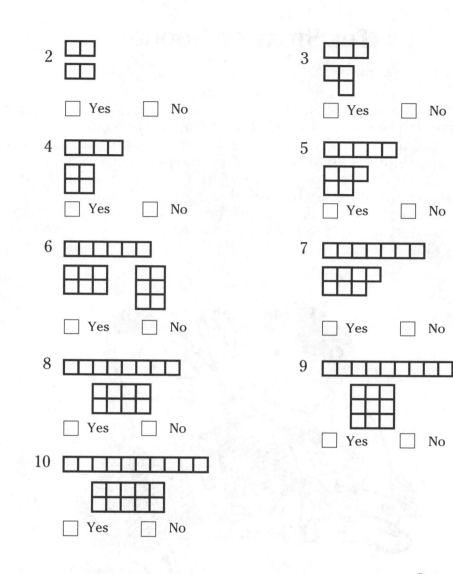

2 ☐ Yes   ☐ No

3 ☐ Yes   ☐ No

4 ☐ Yes   ☐ No

5 ☐ Yes   ☐ No

6 ☐ Yes   ☐ No

7 ☐ Yes   ☐ No

8 ☐ Yes   ☐ No

9 ☐ Yes   ☐ No

10 ☐ Yes   ☐ No

COMPUTERS HAVE DISCOVERED VERY LARGE PRIME NUMBERS. A SUPERCOMPUTER IN MINNESOTA RECENTLY SOUGHT OUT THE LARGEST PRIME NUMBER FOUND SO FAR. IT'S 2 MULTIPLIED BY ITSELF 859,433 TIMES, MINUS 1. THAT NUMBER HAS 258,716 DIGITS. IT'S SO BIG THAT YOUR NEWSPAPER WOULD NEED EIGHT PAGES TO PRINT IT.

THE STORY OF GOOGOL

One of the highest numbers that has a name is the googol. A googol is 1 followed by 100 zeros. A 9-year-old boy invented that name.

At the beginning of this century, an American mathematician, Edward Kasner, was thinking about names for the very highest numbers. His nephew, Milton Sirotta, had a suggestion for a good word: *googol*. He thought the word was funny because it sounded like baby talk.

Then he suggested the name googolplex for an even higher number, 1 followed by a googol of zeros. That's 1 followed by 10,000 zeros, a truly mind-boggling number.

NOW THE WORDS THAT THE 9-YEAR-OLD MATH WHIZ INVENTED HAVE ENTERED INTO MANY OTHER LANGUAGES. SAY "GOOGOL" OR "GOOGOLPLEX," AND YOU COULD BE TALKING TO AN ASTRONOMER IN ENGLISH, HEBREW, CHINESE, OR RUSSIAN.

COUNT AS HIGH AS ANYONE HAS EVER COUNTED

To tell the distances in outer space, astronomers use really big numbers. Some are difficult to imagine if you're standing here on earth.

Think about these numbers. If you look at the word forms, you can almost tell how big some of these numbers are:

Million is 1 followed by 6 zeros.
Billion is 1 with 9 zeros.
Trillion is 1 with 12 zeros.
Quadrillion is 1 with 15 zeros.
Quintillion is 1 with 18 zeros.

Sextillion is 1 with 21 zeros.
Quattuordecillion is 1 with 45 zeros.
Quindecillion is 1 with 48 zeros.
Sexdecillion is 1 with 51 zeros.
Googol is 1 with 100 zeros.

Imagine a number high enough to count all the grains of sand in all the deserts and beaches of the world. Nobody knows what that very high number is, but it is a real number.

Then imagine counting even beyond that number, beyond all the numbers that have names. Imagine counting a number with an endless number of zeros after it.

YOU STILL COULD NOT COUNT AS HIGH AS INFINITY. INFINITY IS NOT A REAL NUMBER. IT'S AN IDEA THAT NUMBERS GO ON FOREVER, WITHOUT END. COUNTING CAN ALWAYS GO HIGHER AND HIGHER AND HIGHER.

The Symbol for Infinity

STRETCH YOUR IMAGINATION

It's very difficult to imagine a googol of anything. You can try, though.

Here's how to stretch your imagination to a googol:

1. Think of atoms. Most of us will never see an atom. To see an atom, a special electronic microscope is needed.

   Atoms are so tiny that a chemist can't separate one into its parts by using ordinary chemistry. Atoms are the smallest particles that can't be divided without losing their special characteristics.

2. Now imagine the opposite of a single atom. Imagine the whole universe, as far as any astronomer has ever observed.

   You know that light waves travel so fast that you can't see them move. Picture the distance that a light wave travels in a whole year. That's a light-year. Then imagine 20 billion light-years. That's how far astronomers have been able to observe the universe stretching beyond our planet Earth.

   (Of course, the universe may go on beyond distances that astronomers have observed. No one knows.)

3. Now picture the number of atoms in that whole vast observable universe.

   An American astronomer, Harry L. Shipman, did the calculating. He believes that the observable universe contains this many atoms: 1 followed by 83 zeros.

   A googol is much bigger. A googol is 1 followed by 100 zeros.

TO IMAGINE A GOOGOL, YOU HAVE TO IMAGINE BEYOND THE WHOLE OBSERVABLE UNIVERSE.

· · · · · · · · · ·
COUNT YOUR OWN ATOMS
· ·

Like every other part of the universe, you are made up of atoms.

As you grow up, you are adding atoms, as well as adding pounds or kilograms. Atoms are so small that, as you grow, you are adding atoms every minute.

Suppose you gain 5 pounds this year. That's about 2.25 kilograms. Now imagine how many atoms you are adding per minute.

Figure you added a sextillion of atoms in 1 minute. A sextillion is 1 with 21 zeros after it.

Do some exercises or play a long outside game. Perhaps you'll lose a sextillion of atoms.

YOU PROBABLY ADDED OR LOST MORE THAN A SEXTILLION ATOMS JUST DURING THE TIME IT TOOK YOU TO THINK ABOUT IT.

ANSWERS FOR SECTION 11: COUNT OLD, COUNT NEW, COUNT ALL AROUND THE WORLD

Spend a Day in Counting School:

Step 1. $60 \times 60 = 3,600$ numbers after 1 hour

Step 2. $3,600 \times 6 = 21,600$ after a 6-hour school day

Step 3. $21,600 \times 5 = 108,000$ after a 5-day school week

Step 4. $1,000,000 \div 108,000 =$ about 9.3 weeks of school

Step 5. $9.3 \times 1,000 = 9,300$ weeks
9,300 weeks $\div 52 = 178.8$ years

Do a Lot of Homework:

Step 1. $11 \times 1,000,000 = 11,000,000$ inches
$28 \times 1,000,000 = 28,000,000$ centimeters

Step 2. $11,000,000$ inches $\div 12 = 916,667$ feet (rounded off)
$28,000,000$ centimeters $\div 100 = 280,000$ meters

Step 3. $916,667$ feet $\div 5,280 = 174$ miles
$280,000$ meters $\div 1,000 = 280$ kilometers

Do Too Much Homework:

Step 2. $2 \times 5 + 3 = 13$ hours of homework a week

Step 3. 4×13 hours $= 52$ pages of homework each week

Step 4.   40 weeks in a school year $\times 52$ pages of homework each week $= 2,080$ pages of homework each school year

Step 5. $1,000,000 \div 2,080 = 481$ years

Step 6.   If there are 20 people in your class, then
481 years $\div 20$ people in the class $= 24$ years per person

Pile Up a Million Dollars:

Step 1. $100 \times 100 = 10,000$

Step 2. $1,000,000 \div 10,000 = 100$ grocery bags

. . . .

ANSWERS FOR SECTION 11
continued

Swim with the Millionaires:

Step 1.   100 dollar bills per inch × 12 inches = $1,200 per foot

Step 2.   2 × 8 = 16 piles along one side of the room
4 × 8 = 32 piles along another side of the room

Step 3.   16 × 32 = 512 piles in all

Step 4. $1,200 × 512 = $614,400

Step 5. $614,400 × 6 = $3,686,400, approaching 4 million dollars

Grow a Farm of Flowers:

Step 2:   Suppose you counted 10 flowers per square foot or 40 flowers per square meter.

Step 3.   10 flowers per square foot × 43,560 square feet per acre = 435,600 flowers for 1 acre
40 flowers per square meter × 10,000 square meters per hectare = 400,000 flowers for 1 hectare

Step 4.   1,000,000 ÷ 435,600 ≈ 20.7 acres to grow a million flowers
1,000,000 ÷ 400,000 ≈ 2.5 hectares to grow a million flowers

Grow in a Row:

Step 1:   Suppose you counted 6 flowers in 1 foot or 20 flowers in 1 meter.

Step 2.   6 flowers × 5,280 = 31,680 flowers in 1 mile
20 flowers × 1,000 = 20,000 flowers in 1 kilometer

Step 3.   1,000,000 ÷ 31,680 ≈ 31.57 miles of flowers
1,000,000 ÷ 20,000 = 50 kilometers of flowers

Solve a Prime Mystery:

Step 3.   Three is a prime number. Six is not a prime number. The first seven prime numbers are 2, 3, 5, 7, 11, 13, 17, and 19.

12. SHARE THE BEST ALL-TIME MATH SECRETS

*Y*ou can be your own calculator. You can learn to figure with your fingers. You can create a triangle that figures for you and even predicts chances.

You can design your own math shortcuts. You can prove you're smarter than a computer.

You can even play a few calculating tricks. These are the best all-time math secrets.

DISCOVER THE VALUE OF NOTHING

Imagine not knowing anything about zero. Zero is a brilliant idea. Actually, zero is not just nothing. A math whiz can use zero as a real number.

A math whiz from long, long ago must have thought of zero. It was most likely a Hindu astonomer of ancient India, but no one knows the name of this clever person.

Suddenly, people must have found adding and subtracting, multiplying and dividing, easier than ever before.

Other ancient people had a concept of zero, even if they had no symbol for it. The ancient Chinese, for instance, lined up numbers by place values: ones, tens, hundreds, and so on. Suppose they had a number like 108. Instead of a zero, they held the tens place with a blank or sometimes a slash mark.

Try adding and subtracting with different kinds of numbers. You'll see the difference that zero makes.

Here's how to prove the value of zero for yourself:

1. Try Roman numeral problems:

CV – XC =

CCVIII + XX =

2. Try the Chinese method of holding a place with a slash mark:

$$1 \setminus 4\,7 \qquad\qquad 5 \setminus \setminus 4\,9$$
$$-\,9 \setminus 3 \qquad\qquad +3\,7\,6 \setminus 1$$

3. Try Arabic number problems:

$$1{,}004 \qquad\qquad 15{,}800$$
$$-\,100 \qquad\qquad +2{,}002$$

THE ARABIC PEOPLE LIKED THE ANCIENT HINDU NUMBER IDEAS SO MUCH THAT THEY TOOK THESE CONCEPTS AS THEIR OWN. EVENTUALLY, SO DID ALL OF EUROPE. NOW MOST PEOPLE USE ARABIC NUMBERS BUT NEVER REMEMBER WHERE THOSE NUMBERS REALLY BEGAN.

· · · · · · · · · ·
PROVE YOU'RE SMARTER
THAN A COMPUTER

· ·

You're more of a math whiz than a computer. One reason is that you can tell what's important and what's not important about numbers.

Here's one way to prove you're smarter:

1. Just glance at this number:

1,992,897.41

2. Round off the number. You can round if off to the nearest million, if you wish. Begin by looking at the far left number. For the purposes of rounding off, ignore the two numbers to the far right. After all, which is more important, a million or two or 0.41?

A COMPUTER OR CALCULATOR CAN ROUND OFF NUMBERS, BUT ONLY IF YOU SET IT TO DO THAT JOB. ON ITS OWN, A COMPUTER DEALS WITH 0.41 AS IF IT WERE JUST AS IMPORTANT AS THE 1 IN THE MILLIONS PLACE. A COMPUTER DOESN'T KNOW WHAT NUMBERS REALLY MEAN THE WAY YOU DO.

THINK LIKE A MATH WHIZ

One day many years ago, the children in a school in Germany had all been very noisy. The teacher was tired. He thought of a way to keep the children quiet.

The children were told to sit down and write out the answer to a very long problem. They were to add all the numbers and find the total of 1 + 2 + 3 + 4 + 5 + 6 . . . all the way to 100.

All this addition was supposed to take a very long time. But a boy named Carl was quiet for only a minute. Then he sprang up with the answer.

How did he solve the problem? He had the idea of lining up the numbers in different ways.

Here's how you can come up with the same quick answer:

1. First imagine the numbers all in a row:

   1 + 2 + 3 . . . all the way to . . . + 98 + 99 + 100

2. Then imagine the numbers all in a row in the other direction:

   100 + 99 + 98 . . . all the way to . . . + 3 + 2 + 1

3. Now picture the numbers in these two rows arranged in columns:

   $$\begin{array}{cccccc} 1 & +\ 2 & +\ 3 \ldots & +\ 98 & +99 & +\ 100 \\ 100 & +99 & +98 \ldots & +\ 3 & +\ 2 & +\quad 1 \end{array}$$

4. Add a few of the columns. You'll notice something amazing. Every single one adds up to the same number.

5. Multiply that sum by the number of columns in each row.

Hint: You know there are 100 numbers in each row. The columns are just another way of organizing the numbers in the rows.

6. To find the sum of one row of numbers, divide the sum for the two rows by 2.

THE YOUNG MATH WHIZ WAS CARL FRIEDRICH GAUSS (1776–1855). HE GREW UP TO BE A FAMOUS MATH-EMATICIAN. YOU CAN USE HIS IDEA TO ADD ANY REGULAR SERIES OF NUMBERS.

THE STORY OF (HUMAN) CALCULATORS

You probably like to go to magic shows. In another century, you might have gone to marvel at a sort of magician called a lightning calculator.

People in the audience asked math questions, and the lightning calculator would tell them the answers almost immediately.

Someone would call out a 40-digit number, and the human calculator would call it right back, only backwards.

People could find out the number of seconds in a year or the number of ounces in a ton or the value of pi to the 1,000th place. The human calculator could multiply a seven-digit number by an eight-digit number in a second.

How did lightning calculators work?

Some had astounding memories. All of them knew math shortcuts plus a few tricks. They might gain time, for instance, by repeating the question or pretending not to hear, all the while calculating the answer.

Carl Friedrich Gauss, the boy math genius, was a lightning calculator who never went on stage. This great man used his math wizardry to do important work and to help other people.

Some other lightning calculators, though, were very strange people.

For instance, Jedediah Buxton was a poor farmer who lived in England two centuries ago. He never learned to read or write, and he could not even write numbers on paper. But he could answer any question people asked him about numbers, even if the question was ridiculous. For instance, he could tell the number of hair widths in a large field. (Of course, no one wanted to check his figures on the hair widths, but everyone assumed he was right.)

Once, some people who wanted to be friends with the poor farmer gave him a rare treat. They took him to a theater in London to hear David Garrick, the greatest actor of his time, play Shakespeare's Richard III.

At the end of the play, Buxton told his friends that the actors had spoken 14,445 words and taken 5,202 steps.

The Story of (Human) Calculators
continued

He had no idea about the plot of the play, and he had not noticed that he was hearing a great actor. He was too busy counting.

Not too many years ago, people who were good with numbers worked as "calculators" and "computers." They did accounts and scientific calculating all day long. You won't be surprised to hear that most of them have now been replaced by machines.

THESE DAYS YOU HARDLY EVER SEE A LIGHTNING CALCULATOR ON STAGE. PERHAPS MACHINES HAVE REPLACED THEM, TOO.

DESIGN YOUR OWN MATH SHORTCUTS

You probably can't go on stage as a lightning calculator. Nevertheless, you'll find the ability to calculate quickly of great use in real life, even if your calculating isn't done quite at the speed of lightning.

Here are some of the best math shortcuts:

1. Look for patterns in numbers. That's fun, and you'll learn more about how numbers work.

   For instance, try multiplying a lot of numbers by 11. You'll see a useful pattern:

$$11 \times 12 = 132$$
$$11 \times 13 = 143$$
$$11 \times 14 = 154$$
$$11 \times 15 = 165$$

In your answers, look for the numbers 12, 13, 14, and 15. Then look at the middle digit of each answer. What can you add to get that middle number?

Try multiplying 11×16 in your head.

2. Play with numbers for fun. Get out a pencil and paper, and try lining up numbers in different ways.

· · · · · · · · · ·
DESIGN YOUR OWN MATH SHORTCUTS
continued

For instance, add even numbers (such as 2, 4, 6, 8) plus even numbers. See if your answers are all alike in some way.

Add odd numbers (such as 1, 3, 5, 7) plus odd numbers. Again, see if your answers are all alike in some way.

Then try adding an even-numbered string of even numbers and odd numbers (such as 2 + 3 + 5 + 6). Try an odd-numbered string of even numbers and odd numbers (such as 1 + 3 + 4 + 6 + 7). See if you can find a pattern in your answers.

3. Round off numbers, and estimate numbers.

Suppose you want to divide 103 by 52. You could begin by dividing 100 by 50. That answer, 2, would give you an immediate idea of the answer to the more difficult problem.

In real life, a rounded-off answer is often good enough.

4. Change numbers around, especially decimals to fractions and fractions to decimals.

Suppose you want to multiply 12 by 0.26. Change the 0.26 to the fraction 1/4. Then divide 12 into four parts. You have a rounded-off answer: 3.

5. Memorize. The patterns in numbers often make memorizing easy.

: **NOW YOU CAN GO ON TO INVENT A**
: **FEW MATH SHORTCUTS OF YOUR**
: **OWN.**

THE STORY OF A MATH WHIZ WHO WASN'T THAT SMART AFTER ALL

The story is that a math whiz of long ago did a favor for a rich and powerful king. The king offered him a reward, anything he wanted.

The math whiz said that he was a humble man and really wanted nothing at all.

The king insisted.

Finally, the math whiz asked the mighty king for one piece of grain. Then the next day he would like double that amount, then double again, then another double, and so on.

At first, the king thought that the math whiz was very humble indeed to be happy with just a few pieces of grain.

You can see trouble coming, though. You know how multiplication works. The pieces of grain, doubled every day, added up fast. Soon the math whiz would lay his hands on all the grain in the kingdom.

Before long, he would own all the grain in the world. Meanwhile, he was making the king feel stupid.

PERHAPS THE MATH WHIZ IN THIS STORY WASN'T ALL THAT SMART. THE KING MIGHT DO THE SAME DOUBLING AND REDOUBLING WITH A JAIL SENTENCE.

PLAY A BIRTHDAY TRICK

This is a new version of an old trick. It never was, and still isn't, a very nice trick to play on anyone.

When your mom or dad asks what you want for your birthday, ask for just one cent 3 weeks in advance. The next day you want just double that amount, and the day after you want another double. Then you want another and another, every day until your birthday.

Would your parents agree? Let's hope they catch on right away. You wouldn't want your parents to be cheated, even by you.

Here's how to count down 21 days until your birthday (use a calculator if you wish):

Day 21   1 cent ($0.01)
Day 20   2 × $0.01 = _____
Day 19   2 × _____ = _____
Day 18   2 × _____ = _____
Day 17   2 × _____ = _____
Day 16   2 × _____ = _____
Day 15   2 × _____ = _____
Day 14   2 × _____ = _____
Day 13   2 × _____ = _____
Day 12   2 × _____ = _____
Day 11   2 × _____ = _____
Day 10   2 × _____ = _____
Day 9   2 × _____ = _____
Day 8   2 × _____ = _____
Day 7   2 × _____ = _____
Day 6   2 × _____ = _____
Day 5   2 × _____ = _____
Day 4   2 × _____ = _____
Day 3   2 × _____ = _____
Day 2   2 × _____ = _____
Your birthday 2 ×   = _____

HOW LONG WOULD IT BE BEFORE YOU HAD $1 MILLION FOR YOUR BIRTHDAY? HOW LONG BEFORE YOU WERE UP TO MORE MONEY THAN THERE IS IN THE WHOLE WORLD? STOP!

PLAY AROUND WITH A VERY PECULIAR NUMBER

You might like this number:

142,857.

Math wizards from all over the world like it because it falls into such interesting patterns.

Use your calculator to do the following multiplications, and look for something odd about each answer:

1. $142,857 \times 2 =$
2. $142,857 \times 3 =$
3. $142,857 \times 4 =$
4. $142,857 \times 5 =$
5. $142,857 \times 6 =$
6. $142,857 \times 7 =$
7. $142,857 \times 8 =$
8. $142,857 \times 9 =$

JUST KEEP MULTIPLYING. YOU'LL FIND A PECULIAR CHANGE EVERY TIME.

FIGURE WITH YOUR FINGERS

Here's a math whiz secret from long, long ago. You can figure with your fingers.

Here's how to use your fingers to multiply by 9:

1. Hold your hands in front of you, with your fingers straight.

   Imagine a number for each of your fingers (including the thumbs) from left to right: 1 for the little finger of your left hand, 2 for your left ring finger, and on to 10 for the little finger on your right hand.

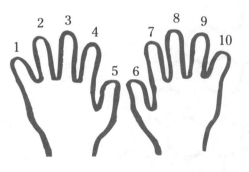

2. Begin with this problem: $9 \times 2 = \square$.
   Bend in the #2 finger. (That's the ring finger on your left hand.) Count the fingers on each side of it: 1 to the left, 8 to the right. That's the answer.

3. Try this problem: $9 \times 6 = \square$.
   Bend in the #6 finger. (That's your right thumb.) Count the fingers on each side of it: 5 to the left, 4 to the right. Put the two digits together. That's the answer.

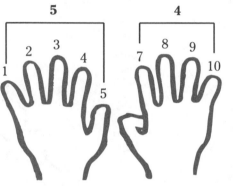

   Perhaps you're beginning to see the pattern.

4. Try another way to remember how to multiply 9's. When you multiply 9 by another number, look at the answer. The number in the tens place and the number in the units place of the answer will always add up to the same number.

   Try these to see:

   $9 \times 8 = \square$ $9 \times 4 = \square$

YOU CAN FIND ANOTHER PATTERN, TOO. WHEN YOU MULTIPLY BY 9, LOOK AT THE TENS PLACE IN THE ANSWER. THAT NUMBER IS ALWAYS THE NUMBER YOU ARE MULTIPLYING BY, MINUS ONE.

MAKE YOUR OWN MATH WHIZ TRIANGLE

This math whiz triangle is 2,200 years old, maybe even older. We know about it first from a mathematician named Halayudha, who lived in ancient India, and then from a Chinese book printed in 1303.

The credit usually goes, though, to the French mathematician Blaise Pascal, who lived more than 300 years ago. Although Pascal may not have invented the triangle, he made it popular. It usually goes by the name Pascal's triangle.

Every math whiz ought to have a triangle like this.

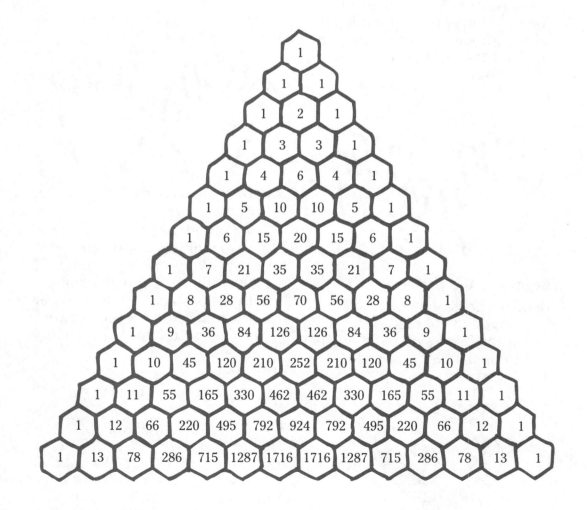

MAKE YOUR OWN MATH WHIZ TRIANGLE
continued

Here's how to make a math whiz triangle (use a calculator if you wish):

1. If you want to play with the numbers inside a very big triangle, get a large piece of plain paper or graph paper. (Actually, though, your triangle can be any size you wish.) Write the number 1 at the top center.

2. Imagine a 0 on each side of the 1.

   Add first to the left: 0 + 1 = 1. Insert that answer below and between the 0 and the 1.

   Then go back and add to the right: 1 + 0 = 1. Insert that answer below the 1 and between the 1 and the 0.

   You have the second row of the triangle.

3. For the third row, again imagine a zero on each side of the row. Add 0 + 1. Write the 1 below and between the 0 and the 1. Now add 1 + 1. Write the 2 below and between the two 1s. Add on the right; 1 + 0 =1. Write down the 1.

4. Keep going in the same way, adding to the right and left as you work your way down the triangle. If you need help, look at the diagram.

You can keep going on and on, building your triangle bigger and bigger.

5. If you want your triangle to be especially fancy, put your numbers into small circles, squares, or hexagons. You may want to make a small stencil to trace around.

: **NOW GO ON TO FIND PATTERNS OF**
: **NUMBERS INSIDE YOUR TRIANGLE.**

PLAY WITH YOUR TRIANGLE

You can play with your math whiz triangle. You can find out patterns of numbers. You can make the triangle into your own home-made calculator.

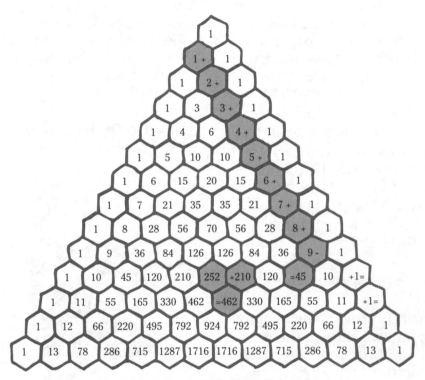

Add Numbers with Your Triangle

Here's how to play with your triangle:

1. To begin, look at any number in the triangle. That number tells the number of different paths from that point to the top of the triangle.

2. Find a line of numbers that runs diagonally down the right side of the triangle. (The line can be short or long or in between.)

   For example, look at the diagonal line that reads 1 + 2 + 3 + 4 + 5 + 6 + 7 + 8 + 9.

   Find the number just below and to the left of the last number, 9. That's the sum of that line of numbers. You've just added them up automatically.

3. Find a line of numbers that runs diagonally down the left side of the triangle. Look at the number just below it and to the right. You've found another sum.

4. Try adding two numbers in a straight row.

For example, look at 252 + 210. You'll find the answer just below and between the two numbers.

5. Look at diagonal lines of numbers, from left to right. You can find a pattern of diagonal lines that add up to Fibonacci numbers.

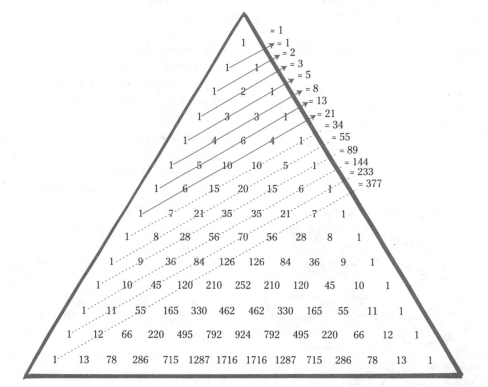

Find Fibonacci Numbers

Hint: Remember that the Fibonacci numbers begin like this: 1, 1, 2, 3, 5, 8, 13, 21, 34, 55, 89.

YOU CAN SEE THESE PATTERNS ALL THE WAY ALONG YOUR TRIANGLE. MAKE A BIGGER TRIANGLE, AND THE PATTERNS WILL SHOW UP IN THAT ONE, TOO.

....
COLOR YOUR TRIANGLE
....

Here's another way to play with your triangle: color it. You'll find interesting shapes and patterns.

Here's how to color your triangle:

1. Use coloring pens, pencils, or crayons. Color the even numbers yellow. Those are the numbers that you can divide evenly by 2.

2. Look for the numbers that you can divide evenly by 3. Color them blue. For some numbers, you must color blue directly over yellow.

3. Look for the numbers that you can divide evenly by 5. Color them red. For some numbers, you must color red directly over yellow or over blue.

4. Look for the numbers that you can divide by both 2 and 3. You'll see that now they have become the same blended color.

5. Look for the numbers that you can divide by both 3 and 5. You'll see that now they have become the same blended color.

6. Look for the numbers that you can divide by both 2 and 5. You'll see that now they have become the same blended color.

:
: **GO ON TO USE YOUR TRIANGLE TO**
: **MAKE PREDICTIONS.**
:

TAKE CHANCES WITH YOUR TRIANGLE

Use your triangle to figure chances and make predictions.

Try it with tossing coins. You can look at your triangle and figure your chances for heads or tails.

You'll need a pencil and paper to keep score.

Here's how to use your triangle to figure chances:

1. Toss a coin once. The coin can come up head or tail. There are only two possibilities.

   Look at the second straight row of your triangle. There are the two possibilities.

2. Now toss two coins. (Or toss one coin twice.)

   Look at the third row of your triangle, and you'll see your chances:

   • 1 possibility that both throws will come up heads

   • 2 possibilities for 1 head and 1 tail

   • 1 possibility that both throws will come up tails

3. Try tossing five coins. (Or toss one coin five times.) Now the possibilities are getting interesting.

   Look at the sixth line of your triangle, and you'll see your chances:

   • 1 possibility that all 5 throws will be heads

   • 5 possibilities for 1 head and 4 tails

   • 10 possibilities for 2 heads and 3 tails

   • 10 possibilities for 3 heads and 2 tails

   • 5 possibilities for 4 heads and 1 tail

   • 1 possibility that all 5 throws will be tails

4. As your chances become more complicated, try drawing a grid. Write H for heads and T for tails. Make your guesses, and the triangle will help you. Look in the row that is the same number as your coin toss plus one.

YOU CAN TOSS COINS MORE AND MORE. MAKE AS MANY TOSSES AS YOU LIKE. YOUR TRIANGLE WILL ALWAYS HELP YOU TO PREDICT THE OUTCOMES.

ANSWERS FOR SECTION 12: SHARE THE BEST ALL-TIME MATH SECRETS

Discover the Value of Nothing:

Step 1.　CV (105) – XC (90) = XV 15

　　　　CCVIII (208) + XX (20) = (CCXXVIII) 228

Step 2.　1\47 (1,047) – 9\3 (903) = 144

　　　　5\\49 (50,049) + 376\1 (37,601) = 87,650

Step 3.　1,004 – 100 = 904

　　　　15,800 + 2,002 = 17,802

Prove You're Smarter Than a Computer:

Round off at 2 million.

Think Like a Math Whiz:

Step 4.　Every column adds up to 101.

Step 5.　$101 \times 100 = 10,100$

Step 6.　10,100 / 2 = 5,050

Design Your Own Math Shortcuts:

Step 1.　Arrive at the middle digit by adding the two digits in the number you are multiplying 11 by:

　　　　In 132: 1 + 2 = 3

　　　　In 143: 1 + 3 = 4

　　　　In 154: 1 + 4 = 5

　　　　In 165: 1 + 5 = 6

　　　　$11 \times 16 = 176$

　　　　In 176: 1 + 6 = 7

Step 2.　Add even numbers, and your answer will always be an even number. Add odd numbers, and your answer will always be an odd number.

Step 3.　103 ÷ 52 = 1.98

Step 4.　$12 \times 0.26 = 3.12$

Play a Birthday Trick:

$10,485.76 at your birthday

By the 28th day, you'd be above a million: $1,342,177.28.

Play Around with a Very Peculiar Number:

Step 1. $142,857 \times 2 = 285,714$
The answer repeats the number you multiplied, except that the 14 has moved to the far right.

Step 2. $142,857 \times 3 = 428,571$
The answer is the same except that the 1 has moved to the far right.

Step 3. $142,857 \times 4 = 571,428$
The 5 and 7 have pushed their way to the beginning of the number.

Step 4. $142,857 \times 5 = 714,285$
Again, the numbers are the same, but they have changed positions. The 7 has moved to the far left.

Step 5. $142,857 \times 6 = 857,142$
The first three numbers have switched positions with the last three.

Step 6. $142,857 \times 7 = 999,999$
You're right on the edge of 1 million.

Step 7. $142,857 \times 8 = 1,142,856$
The last number, 7, seems to split into 6 and 1. The 6 stays at the end. The 1 goes to the beginning.

Step 8. $142,857 \times 9 = 1,285,713$
The missing 4 splits into 1 and 3 and goes to the end.

Figure with Your Fingers:

Step 2. $9 \times 2 = 18$
Step 3. $9 \times 6 = 54$
Step 4. $9 \times 8 = 72$, and $7 + 2 = 9$
$9 \times 4 = 36$, and $3 + 6 = 9$

Color Your Triangle:

Step 4. Yellow and blue mix to become green.
Step 5. Blue and red mix to become violet.
Step 6. Yellow and red mix to become orange.

13. THINK LIKE A COMPUTER

Put your imagination into a machine. You'll find some serious limits.

You can operate with only two numbers. You really can't think at all.

But you can speed through numbers, and you can feel their power.

You can even build your own abacus, a computing machine of your own.

THINK ONE, THINK TWO

Like many other peoples of ancient times, the Bacairis of ancient Brazil counted with only two numbers. They had two number words: *takala* for the number 1 and *ahage* for the number 2.

Think what you'd do if you were an ancient Brazilian with three pots to trade. You could trade each pot for two braided belts or one sack of grain.

You might have to bring out the pots just one or two at a time. You'd have to count the six braided belts or the three sacks just one or two at a time. You'd have a hard time remembering belts, sacks, and pots.

With so few numbers on hand, your thinking would get fuzzy. You might wish you had something modern to help you—such as a computer.

Here's how a computer could help, even with only two numbers:

1. First reduce the problem to a code.

1 pot (P) = 2 belts (B)

1 pot (P) = 1 sack of grain (S)

2. Now set up all the possibilities, just as a computer could.

Begin with trading all the pots only for braided belts. That's one possibility:

1P + 1P + 1P = 2B + 2B + 2B

Now consider trading all the pots only for sacks of grain. That's a second possibility:

1P + 1P + 1P = 1S + 1S + 1S

Now figure out the other possibilities.

Hint: If you don't care in what order you trade your pots, then there are only four possible combinations of belts and sacks. Two of them are given above.

3. Now decode the answers. The people who develop computer codes have to make sure that, in the end, the code can be translated back into human words and numbers.

Figure out a way to tell how many braided belts and/or sacks of grain you ought to take home in exchange for your three pots.

IN TIME, THE BACAIRI PEOPLE CAME UP WITH TWO MORE IDEAS ABOUT NUMBERS. MAKAGURAGA WAS THE WORD FOR "MANY." MAKAAGURAGA MEANT "VERY MANY."

....

PLAY A HUMAN COMPUTER GAME

....

Computers work with a code of 0's and 1's.

A complex series of 0's and 1's signal electric switches to turn on and off. The switches flip-flop from ON (1) to OFF (0) and back again, with a speed no human being can match.

When you type instructions into a computer, the computer changes all that information into 0's and 1's, complex ON-and-OFF patterns. (The basic instructions are the program.)

Suppose, like a computer, you had only two "ideas." You could play a game with only two words: YES and NO.

This is a version of a time-honored game, good for playing on long road trips.

Here's how to play the game:

1. One player, the "computer," thinks of a number.

2. The second player finds out the number by asking questions. The "computer" can answer each question only with YES or NO. Those are the only two words allowed.

3. If you are the second player, how do you guess the number? Ask math questions. Ask whether this is an odd number or a number you can divide by 5. Be sure to phrase each question so that the "computer" can answer YES or NO.

IF YOU GUESS THE NUMBER IN 20 QUESTIONS, YOU WIN. THEN YOU GET TO BE THE "COMPUTER."

COLOR A TAX CODE

More than 600 years ago, the rulers of Russia figured out a way to write taxes.

They wrote in a code that looks almost like pictures.

Most codes are used to keep a secret, but the Russian rulers didn't care about that. They knew the people hated to pay taxes. (Their taxes were very high and very unfair.) The elaborate code was used so that the people couldn't change the amount of their taxes.

When you write taxes the way those Russian rulers did, use coloring pens or pencils. These dreadful taxes ought at least to look colorful and beautiful.

The taxes you will write are for a rich family that owes 5,638 rubles and 43 kopecks.

Here's how to write the taxes:

1. At the top of the paper, draw a row of six-pointed stars, each with a cross inside. Draw one star for each 1,000 rubles. (Be careful to draw just the number of stars you need, no more. You'll need to do some figuring.)

2. On the second line, draw a wheel with a cross inside, and over the cross put an X for the spokes of the wheel. Draw one wheel for each 100 rubles.

3. On the third line, draw a square for each 10 rubles.

4. On the fourth line, draw an X for each one ruble.

5. Now figure out the kopecks. In those days 100 kopecks added up to one ruble, in the same way that 100 cents add up to one dollar. On the fifth line, for each 10 kopecks, draw nine slanted lines with a line through the middle. You'll need four of these symbols.

6. On the sixth line, draw one slanted line for each one kopeck.

The Tax Accountant for One Rich Family

FINISH BY DRAWING A THICK BORDER AROUND YOUR TAX CODE. THE RUSSIANS DID THAT AS ONE MORE WAY TO KEEP PEOPLE FROM MAKING SNEAKY LITTLE CHANGES. THESE LONG-AGO NUMBER CODES WERE AMONG THE BEGINNINGS OF THE IDEA OF CALCULATORS AND COMPUTERS.

THE STORY OF COUNTERS

Imagine what it would be like to be afraid of numbers.

Suppose you couldn't read or count. In ancient times, you might have found yourself standing in front of a sort of judge, called a counter. He would be sitting at a counting table and working with a counting board, something like an abacus.

The counter would be working the beads or the sticks with astonishing speed. You might have found yourself staring at the flying fingers.

"This is how much you owe!" the counter would say. "These are your taxes!"

How could you argue? The counter had the magic of numbers.

We still use the same word, *counter,* for the work table in a store or a kitchen. Strangely enough, the word no longer has much to do with counting, though counting still goes on in a store or a kitchen. No one fears a counter any more.

If you ever hear a high price blamed on "the computer," though, you might think back a few thousand years and imagine how your ancestors might have felt.

THE ANCIENT COUNTERS COULD HAVE RUN RACES WITH OUR OWN MODERN CALCULATORS AND COMPUTERS, WITH NO FEAR AT ALL.

········
BUILD YOUR OWN ABACUS
····································

The abacus makes a good sort of calculator, so good that after the Chinese invented it, people from all over the world took up the idea.

In many places, people prefer the abacus to other calculators or computers. They think the abacus is faster—and more fun.

Here's how to build and decorate your own abacus.

Here's what you need:

2 large pieces of corrugated cardboard

A pen or pencil

A ruler

A triangle

A craft knife

A wire cutter

Safety goggles

1 package of #18 wire flower stems, available from a hobby store, the craft section of a department store, or a florist

1 package of 6-millimeter, multicolored, faceted beads, available from a hobby store or from the craft section of a department store

Household cement that works on metal and paper

Colored plastic tape, poster paint, fluorescent poster paint, stickers, or other materials to decorate the abacus

. . . .

BUILD YOUR OWN ABACUS
continued

Here's how to make the abacus:

1. Use the ruler and triangle to measure the two pieces of cardboard. Use the craft knife to cut out the two pieces and to cut out two windows in each piece.

   The 9-inch (23 cm) edge ought to run in the same direction as the corrugation. The 7$\frac{1}{2}$-inch (19 cm) edge ought to run against the corrugation.

   > *Caution: You need an adult to help you work with the craft knife.*

   Here's how to measure and cut out the cardboard pieces:

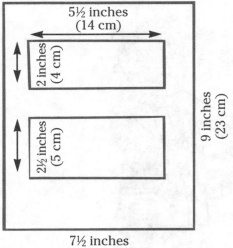

2. On the wrong side of one piece of cardboard, draw 10 vertical lines along the 9-inch (23 cm) side and across the windows. There should be a $\frac{1}{2}$-inch

(1-cm) space between each of the 10 lines.

Here's how the lines should look:

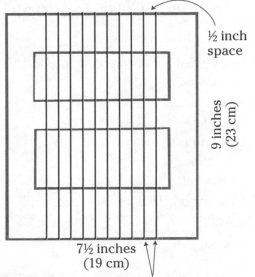

Draw lines evenly spaced for placing beaded wires and reinforcing wires

3. With the wire cutter, cut 12 of the wire flower stems into 8$\frac{1}{2}$-inch (21-cm) lengths.

   > *Caution: You need an adult to help you work with the wire cutter. Use the safety goggles to cover your eyes.*

4. Line up 10 of the wire stems. (You'll have two of the 12 stems left over.) Working from right to left, thread the beads like this:

   - On wire #1, thread 7 beads of one color.

   - On wire #2, thread 7 beads of a second color.

- On wire #3, thread 7 beads of a third color.

- On wire #4, thread 7 beads of a fourth color.

- Leave wire #5 with no beads.

- On wires #6, #7, #8, and #9, thread beads in the same order and same colors as you used for wires #1, #2, #3, and #4.

- On wire #10, thread 7 beads of a different color from all the others.

5. Starting at the right, place a line of the household cement along the first line you drew on the cardboard.

> *Caution: You may need an adult to help you with this step. Use the cement only in a well-ventilated area. Do not breathe the fumes.*

Separate the beads on the first wire so that 2 beads go into the smaller window and 5 beads into the larger window. Carefully lay the wire on the cement line and across the windows of the abacus. Press the wire down evenly.

6. Run cement along the second line, and place the second wire. Continue until you have placed all 10 wires along the 10 lines. On each wire except #5 there should be 2 beads in the smaller window and 5 in the larger window. (Wire #5 has no beads.)

7. Run a line of cement along each 9-inch (23-cm) side of the cardboard. Place the two leftover unbeaded stems along each of those edges. Press down evenly.

These wires will reinforce and strengthen your abacus.

8. Cover all the rest of the inside of the cardboard with cement. Carefully place the second piece of cardboard on top.

9. Set a weight on top, and let the cement dry.

Here's how the abacus should look now:

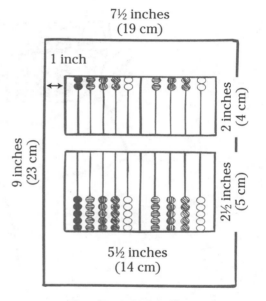

The Completed Abacus Ready to Be Decorated

10. If you wish, bind the edges of the cardboard with the colored plastic tape. Use the poster paints, fluorescent poster paints, or stickers to decorate your abacus. You may want to paint math signs and symbols along the edges.

NOW YOU'VE MADE YOUR OWN ABACUS. GO ON TO SEE WAYS TO PLAY AND WORK WITH IT.

· · · · · · · · · · ·
TELL THE DIFFERENCE BETWEEN
HEAVEN AND EARTH

· ·

Your abacus has beads that live in heaven and beads that live on earth.

Here's how to tell the difference:

1. Hold your abacus so that the smaller window is on top. In that window are the heavenly beads. Down below, in the larger window, are the earthly beads.

   Set up your abacus so that all the heavenly beads are "home," up in heaven (that is, at the top of the window), and all the earthly beads are also "home," down on earth (at the bottom of the window). When the beads are all at home, the abacus says "zero."

TELL THE DIFFERENCE BETWEEN HEAVEN AND EARTH

continued

Place values

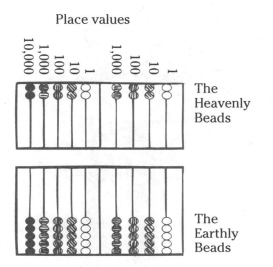

The Heavenly Beads

The Earthly Beads

2. Find numbers on each side of heaven and earth.

The wires and beads have place values. Begin at the right. There's a wire for the ones or units place. Then there are wires for tens, hundreds, and thousands. That's true for both the heavenly beads and the earthly beads.

On the other side of the fifth, or dividing, wire, you have place values again, in the same order and with the same colors. These wires also begin on the right with the ones or units place. Then they go on to tens, hundreds, thousands, and ten thousands.

These place values are marked on the diagram.

What's different about the heavenly beads? Each one is worth 5 times the amount of an earthly bead.

Slide one heavenly bead down, and one earthly bead up, to the center at the ones place.

You have just set up your abacus to 5 + 1, or the number 6.

Return the beads to "home." Now slide a heavenly bead down, and an earthly bead up, at the hundreds places. What number do you have now?

3. Perhaps you'd like to try more numbers on the abacus. For example, try sliding beads up and down to show all the different ways you can set up the number 20.

GO ON TO SET UP MORE AND MORE ABACUS NUMBERS

COUNT ON HEAVEN AND EARTH

Use all your abacus power. You can count on both heaven and earth to help.

Here are numbers you'll like:

1. Use all the beads of your abacus at the same time. Slide all the heavenly beads down. Slide all the earthly beads up. What numbers did you create?

2. Try to set up your abacus to read 99,999 on the left side and 9,999 on the right side.

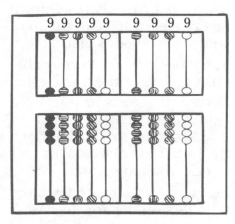

NOW YOU KNOW THE VALUE OF ALL THE BEADS ON YOUR ABACUS.

TRY ABACUS SUBTRACTING

If you lived in China or Japan, you might take lessons in how to use an abacus. The Japanese abacus is different from the Chinese abacus, but either kind works fine. Use your abacus to try a sample problem. You'll learn something about number patterns on an abacus—and in real life, too.

Here's the problem: $25 - 17 = \square$.

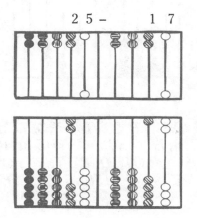

Here's how to solve the problem:

1. Set up 25 on the left side of the abacus.
2. Set up 17 on the right side of the abacus.

   Your abacus looks like this:

3. Now take away (or subtract) numbers on the right side as you create the answer on the left. Begin by subtracting 5 like this:
   • Take away 5 from the ones place on the right side.

• At the same time, subtract 5 from the ones place on the left side.

(Why subtract only 5? That's as much as you can subtract without borrowing.)

Now your problem has become $20 - 12 = \square$.

Your abacus looks like this:

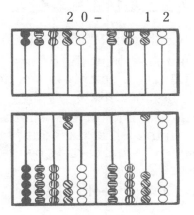

4. To subtract 2 from the ones place, borrow 10 from the tens place. You take 1 ten away from the tens place and add 1 five and 5 ones to the ones place.
   • On the left side in the tens place, slide down 1 earthly bead (10).

. . . .
TRY ABACUS SUBTRACTING
continued

- At the ones place on the left side, slide up 5 earthly beads and slide down 1 heavenly bead (5 + 5 = 10).

  Now your abacus looks like this:

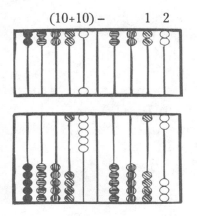

5. Now subtract 12 from 20.

   - On the right at the ones place, slide the 2 earthly beads down to home. (Take away 2.)

   - At the same time, to subtract 2 on the left at the ones place, slide down 2 earthly beads. (20 – 2 = 18).

   Your abacus looks like this:

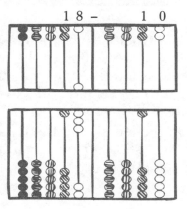

6. Now complete your subtraction problem.

   - At the tens place on the right, slide 1 earthly bead down to home. (On the right side, the beads are all "at home" now. They're at zero.)

   - At the same time, at the tens place on the left, slide 1 earthly bead home.

   Here's how your abacus looks with the answer set up:

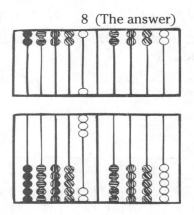

THE ANSWER TO THE PROBLEM IS ON THE LEFT SIDE OF THE ABACUS. LOOK FOR OTHER PATTERNS OF NUMBERS IN YOUR ABACUS. PERHAPS THEY'LL LOOK HEAVENLY.

TRY ABACUS ADDING

Now try adding the same numbers and see what happens. Here's the problem: 25 + 17 = ☐.

Here's how to solve the problem:

1. Set up 25 on the left side and 17 on the right side of the abacus.

   The abacus looks the same as it did for the subtraction problem:

2. When you add on the left side, you must take away the same number on the right. Begin by adding 7 like this:

   - In the ones place on the right, push down 2 earthly beads and push up 1 heavenly bead.

   - As you take away 7 on the right, add 7 on the left side. At the ones place on the left, push up 2 earthly beads and push down 1 heavenly bead.

   Now your problem has become 32 + 10 = ☐.

   Here's how your abacus looks now:

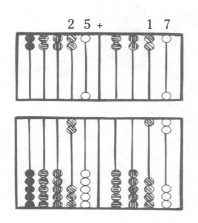

2 5 +   1 7

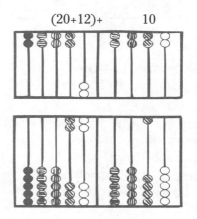

(20+12)+   10

TRY ABACUS ADDING

continued

3. Carry 10 from the ones place to the tens place on the left side. Here's how you do it:

- At the ones place, slide 2 heavenly beads up "to home" (–10).

- At the tens place, move 1 earthly bead up (+10).

Here's how your abacus looks now:

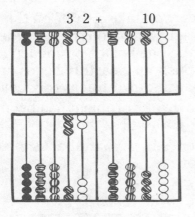

4. Take away 10 from the right side as you add 10 to the left side.

- Take away the 1 earthly bead on the right at the tens place by sliding it down to home. (On the right side, the beads are all "at home" now. They're at zero.)

• Add 1 earthly bead on the left at the tens place by sliding it up.

Here's how your abacus looks with the answer set up:

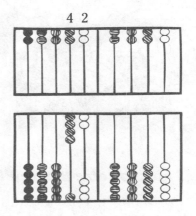

THE ANSWER TO THE PROBLEM IS ON THE LEFT SIDE OF THE ABACUS. IF YOU PRACTICE ENOUGH ON THE ABACUS, YOUR FINGERS WILL FLY. YOU'LL SOLVE PROBLEMS QUICKLY.

COUNT LIKE A COMPUTER

See if you can crack the code that computers use.

The code is only 1's and 0's. Computer code is called a binary system. It uses only two numbers. This makes sense since *bi* is the word for two.

To crack the code, you must translate the whole range of numbers we use into 0's and 1's.

Here's how to crack the code:

1. Look at the chart of 0's and 1's.

32	16	8	4	2	1		
0	0	0	0	0	1	=	1
0	0	0	0	1	0	=	2
0	0	0	0	1	1	=	3
0	0	0	1	0	0	=	4
0	0	0	1	0	1	=	5
0	0	0	1	1	0	=	6
0	0	0	1	1	1	=	7
0	0	1	0	0	0	=	8
0	0	1	0	0	1	=	9
0	0	1	0	1	0	=	10
0	0	1	0	1	1	=	11
0	0	1	1	0	1	=	13
0	0	1	1	1	0	=	14
0	0	1	1	1	1	=	15
1	0	0	1	0	1	=	37
1	0	1	0	0	0	=	40
1	0	1	1	1	1	=	47

The Binary Code

You'll see you can write 4 this way: 100. (The 1 is in the 4 column.)

You can write 8 like this: 1000. (The 1 is in the 8 column.)

2. If you want to translate a code for a number that is not in a horizontal row of numbers, do some adding.

Suppose to crack a code you had to add 2 + 1 = ☐. You wouldn't have any trouble figuring out that the answer is 3.

Even if the code became more difficult, you could still figure out the answer. For example, 32 + 8 + 4 + 2 + 1 = ☐.

Do the same adding on the chart. Notice on the chart that the code for 1 + 2 is the same as the code for 3. The code for 32 + 8 + 4 + 2 + 1 is the same as the code for 47.

3. See if you can crack the code for a number that's not on the chart.

Hint: Don't get the computer code of 1's and 0's confused with the numbers 1 and 0 that people use. For instance, a computer reads our number 10 as 1010. A confused human being might think that code meant 1,010, a thousand and ten. In computer code, though, it's a 1 under the 8 row and a 1 under the 2 row. So a computer reads 10 as 8 + 2.

COMPUTERS CAN HELP YOU TO CALCULATE, WRITE, DRAW, OR PLAY GAMES. BUT THEY CAN'T REALLY THINK. THEY JUST FOLLOW THE CODES THAT PEOPLE DESIGNED. THAT'S WHY HIGH-LEVEL COMPUTER PROGRAMS ARE CALLED ARTIFICIAL INTELLIGENCE, NOT REAL INTELLIGENCE.

ANSWERS FOR SECTION 13:
THINK LIKE A COMPUTER

Think One, Think Two:

Step 2. 1P + 1P + 1P = 2B + 2B + 1S
1P + 1P + 1P = 2B + 1S + 1S

Russian Tax Code

Tell the Difference Between Heaven and Earth:

Step 2. You set 100 with the earthly bead and 500 with the heavenly bead. That makes 600.

Step 3. Here are three ways to set up the number 20:
(1) 2 earthly beads up on the tens wire
(10 + 10 = 20)
(2) 5 earthly beads up on the ones wire
1 heavenly bead down on the ones wire
1 earthly bead up on the tens wire
(5 + 5 + 10 = 20)
(3) 2 heavenly beads down on the ones wire
1 earthly bead up on the tens wire
(5 + 5 + 10 = 20)

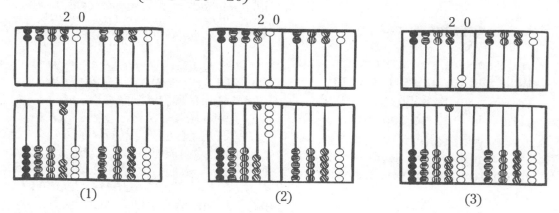

(1)   (2)   (3)

Answers for Section 13:
Think Like a Computer
continued

Count on Heaven and Earth:

Step 1.   If you use all the beads on the left, you have the number 166,665. Count like this: Start at the ones place and move left. Count 15 + 150 + 1,500 + 15,000 + 150,000 = 166,665.
If you use all the beads on the right, you have the number 16,665. Start at the ones place, and count 15 + 150 + 1,500 + 15,000 = 16,665.

Step 2.   To make 99,999 on the left and 9,999 on the right, move down 1 heavenly bead and move up 4 earthly beads at each place.

Try Abacus Subtracting:

On the left side: 25 – 17 = 8
On the right side: 17 – 17 = 0
The answer remaining on the left side is 8.

Try Abacus Adding:

On the left side: 25 + 17 = 42
On the right side: 17 – 17 = 0
The answer remaining on the left side is 42.

Count Like a Computer:

Step 2.   32 + 8 + 4 + 2 + 1 = 47

14. PLAY THE WORLD'S BEST GAMES

Would you like to play a game from New Zealand or Africa—or from another planet?

Would you like to read words on your calculator instead of numbers?

Would you like to keep baseball stats? Would you like to help your team beat a losing streak?

Would you like to design your own games and create your own puzzles? You can even liven up a board game that goes on a little too long.

These are the world's best games.

. . . .

PLAY ON A NEW ZEALAND STAR

. . . .

The Maori people of New Zealand have a game they love. They call it Mu Torere.

Mu Torere is a game of skill and strategy. Two players match wits as each tries to block the other person from playing.

Play the game on a star you design yourself.

Here's how to design your game:

1. Construct an eight-pointed star on a piece of posterboard or cardboard. If you want a simpler game, construct a six-pointed star.

3. Make two sets of markers from pebbles, dried peas or beans, colored glass or plastic pieces, buttons, or coins. Players need distinctive markers so they can

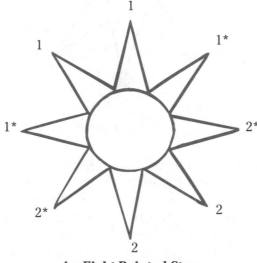

An Eight-Pointed Star

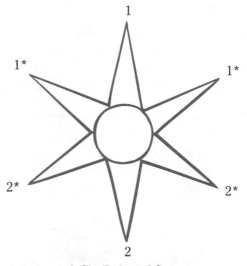

A Six-Pointed Star

Use coloring pens, poster paints, or crayons to decorate your star. You can make the gameboard as plain or as fancy as you wish.

2. If you want to play outdoors, use chalk to draw a star on a sidewalk. Or use a stick to draw a star in dirt or sand. This is a good beach game.

recognize their own by color, size, or shape.

For an eight-pointed star, each player needs four markers. For a six-pointed star, each player needs three markers. (Each player needs half as many markers as there are points to the star.)

PLAY ON A NEW ZEALAND STAR
continued

Here's how to play:

1. Each player puts markers on half the points of the star. Every point should have a marker on it.

2. The first player moves one marker to the center of the star.

3. The next player moves a marker to the empty point of the star.

Rule: In the first two moves, each player can move only outer markers. (On the diagram on page 255, these are shown with an asterisk.)

4. The players take turns moving their markers from one star point to another or from a star point to the center of the star.

Rules: Players can't skip over markers. There can't be two markers on one point at the same time. A player can move only from one point to an adjacent free point or to the center if it is free.

5. The game continues until one player is blocked and cannot move a marker.

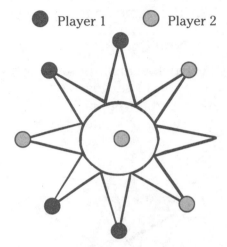

Player 1   Player 2

Player 2 is the winner

Player 1 is blocked and unable to move

Your strategy is to block your opponent by getting your markers on the points surrounding your opponent's markers and by having one marker in the center. When that happens, your opponent cannot move and is blocked from play.

THAT'S HOW YOU WIN AT MU TORERE.

THE STORY OF A GAME THAT ENDS QUARRELING AND STOPS WAR

King Shamba had a problem: his people were always quarreling.

Mainly, they quarreled among themselves, but they also started quarrels with the people of the other kingdoms along the Congo River in Africa. They often urged their king to let them go to war with their neighbors.

They spent most of their time making weapons.

The neighbors were afraid of King Shamba's people. They even called the king's people by the name of their most deadly weapon, a throwing knife called the shongo.

Finally, King Shamba's people no longer had customers to buy their cattle and goats. They could no longer go to nearby farms to buy food. Also, there was no one to sell them the woven clothes and wood carvings they wanted.

King Shamba decided his people needed another, more peaceful way to spend their time. He invented a game.

· · · · · · · · · · ·

THE STORY OF A GAME THAT ENDS QUARRELING AND STOPS WAR
continued

The king's people loved it, and their tempers improved. They stopped quarreling so they would have more time to play. They put away the deadly shongo and made peace with their neighbors.

Soon King Shamba's people started their own farms and grew grain, vegetables, and fruit for themselves. They learned how to weave their own beautiful clothes.

They figured out how to carve wood into works of art. If you ever travel to London, you can see a carved wooden statue of King Shamba in the British Museum. The statue shows the great king seated, with his game in front of him.

King Shamba's game became popular all across Africa, in South America, and then all around the world.

Judges in parts of Africa kept boards in front of them in court. The game reminded them to make fair and just decisions. Governers kept gold boards so they could play the game with their people and become friends with them.

When someone died in South America, friends used to sit by the coffin and play the game. The game was supposed to cheer up the spirit as it made its sad way toward the afterlife.

Even animals like King Shamba's game. The story is that, in the evenings before lions go out to hunt, they use their claws to scratch out a gameboard in the dirt. Then they play the game with little sticks.

YOU'LL PROBABLY LIKE THE AFRICAN STONE GAME, TOO. GO ON TO MAKE YOUR OWN PLAYING BOARD.

MAKE YOUR OWN KING SHAMBA'S GAME

Because this is a favorite game around the world, you can find many different styles of gameboards and ways of playing.

You can play the game outside. Just dig holes in sand or dirt and then find pebbles to use as counters.

Or you can buy beautiful, hand-crafted gameboards.

Or you can make your own personal gameboard and decorate it in your own unique style.

Here's what you need:

An egg carton

Markers, coloring pens, or paints, if you wish

Two small cups or dishes, if you wish

48 counters of whatever kind you want:

Colored beads or small glass counters from a game store

A multi-colored mix of chickpeas, whole dried green peas, mung beans, and other small dried beans or peas

Seeds or very small pebbles

Here's how you get ready to play:

1. If you wish, use the markers, coloring pens, or crayons to decorate the egg carton with your own designs.

   (You probably want to store your counters in the egg carton. If not, you may want to cut off the top of the carton.)

2. Use the small cups or dishes to store your counters when you play. Or just keep your counters on the table at each end of the carton.

3. Count out 48 counters, and you're ready to play.

THIS MAY BE THE WORLD'S OLDEST AND BEST GAME. THEREFORE, IT TAKES MANY FORMS AND GOES BY MANY DIFFERENT NAMES. YOU CAN HEAR IT CALLED OWARI OR WARE (FOR THE SEEDS PEOPLE USE AS COUNTERS) OR MANKALA (FOR THE "TRANSFERRING" PART OF THE GAME). IN PARTS OF AFRICA, KPO IS THE NAME. THIS WORD IS SUPPOSED TO SOUND LIKE SEEDS DROPPING INTO THE CUPS.

PLAY KING SHAMBA'S GAME

The object of this version of the game is to take so many counters that your opponent has no chance to win. You need a fast-counting friend to play the game with you.

Here's how to play:

1. Place the playing board between the two players so that each player faces 6 of the 12 holes.

2. The players place 4 counters in each of the 12 holes. Player B's cups are numbered 1 through 6. Player A's cups are numbered 7 through 12.

3. Player A picks up the counters from one of the 6 holes on the A side and distributes them, moving in a counterclockwise direction, one by one in neighboring holes. (See the arrow in the diagram.)

4. Player A picks up all the counters from the hole into which the last counter drops. Player A then continues to distribute these counters as before.

5. Player A's turn ends in one of two ways:
   - The last counter falls into a cup with no counters in it.
   - The last counter falls into a cup on the B side of the board that contains only 1 or 2 counters (making a total of 2 or 3).

Player A

● Counter

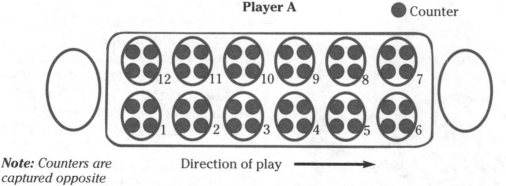

Note: *Counters are captured opposite the direction of play.*

Direction of play ⟶

Player B

Board Setup at Beginning of Game

PLAY KING SHAMBA'S GAME

continued

6. Player A then can capture counters from these cups:

- The last cup into which player A drops a counter
- The cups that immediately precede that last cup and that contain 2 or 3 counters

9. In this polite game, a player does not empty all of an opponent's cups, but leaves a counter in one of them. If player A wins, player B's 6 cups will all be empty. But player B will have emptied them.

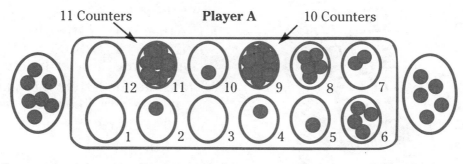

11 Counters   **Player A**   10 Counters

12 11 10 9 8 7

1 2 3 4 5 6

Note: Counters are captured opposite the direction of play.

Direction of play ⟶

Player B

Board Setup During Play

7. Now it's player B's turn. Player B picks up counters from one of the 6 holes on the B side of the board and, like player A, distributes them in a counterclockwise direction.

8. The object is to capture the counters from the opponent's side of the board. When one player has no more counters, the game ends.

AS YOU PRACTICE THE GAME, YOU CAN MOVE FASTER AND FASTER. COUNT QUICKLY, AND LET YOUR FINGERS FLY. THEN YOU'LL WIN.

MAKE YOUR CALCULATOR TALK

Look at the numbers on your calculator. You'll see they are made up of straight lines. For instance, make a row of 8's, and look closely at them. Perhaps you'll see the straight lines: *88888888*

Clear your calculator and put in new numbers. Now turn your calculator upside down, and see if you can find letters.

Here are numbers to "translate" (upside down) into words:

1. 505, a call for help
2. 8075, what your mother thinks when your room is messy
3. 3573, something different
4. 3507, what happens when you don't win the game
5. 7718, a good name
6. 345, when he won't do
7. 8078, the creature that ate Manhattan
8. 0.7734, glad to see you
9. 77345, a beach souvenir
10. 5376606, what to wear when you swim, ski, or drill

Here's how to write your own calculator words:

1. Use these letters to make a word: B, E, G, H, I, L, O, S. (Sorry. You can use only these eight letters.)

2. Translate the letters into calculator numbers, like this:

    0 becomes O.

    1 becomes I.

    3 becomes E.

    4 becomes h.

    5 becomes S.

    6 becomes g.

    7 becomes L.

    8 becomes B.

3. Write your word backwards onto your calculator.

Hint: If your word ends in O, push 0 and then the decimal point. Otherwise, your calculator will erase the 0.

YOU CAN MAKE THIS CALCULATOR GAME MORE COMPLICATED. MAKE UP NUMBER PROBLEMS THAT END NOT JUST IN NUMBERS BUT IN WORDS TOO.

DESIGN MATH WHIZ HIDE AND SEEK

You might call this a math whiz version of hide and seek.

This is a creative sort of game. You and your friends can design it yourselves.

Here's how to design the game:

1. Design a line of numbers. You decide how to create the line. You can count backwards, or you can skip numbers. You can add, subtract, multiply, or divide. You can use large numbers or negative numbers. You can use fractions or decimal points.

The only rule is that the line of numbers must have a sensible pattern.

For example, here's a line of numbers:

$\frac{1}{8}$ $\frac{1}{4}$ $\frac{1}{2}$ 1 2 4 8 16 32 64 128 256

To create this line, you multiply each number by 2 to get the next number.

2. Leave one number out of your sequence. That's the number you're hiding.

3. Have your opponent seek the hidden number.

4. Take turns coming up with a line of numbers. Keep track of each player's solutions.

Each correct answer is worth 10 points.

Each wrong answer is minus 1.

The person with the highest score wins.

YOU'LL NEED TO MAKE YOUR NUMBER SEQUENCES MORE AND MORE COMPLICATED. YOU KNOW THAT HIDE AND SEEK IS BEST WITH REALLY GOOD HIDING PLACES.

LIVEN UP A BOARD GAME

Sometimes Monopoly or other board games can drag on a little too long. Here's a way to make the game more exciting.

Keep a piece of paper by your side as you play. Do a survey to discover the answer to this question:

What space is landed on most often?

YOU'LL PROBABLY FIND THE SPACES ARE NOT ALL EQUAL. THERE'S A HIGHER PERCENTAGE CHANCE THAT YOU'LL LAND ON SOME THAN ON OTHERS. MAYBE YOU CAN FIGURE OUT A REASON.

SELECT AN ALL-STAR PITCHING STAFF

If all baseball and softball pitchers were the same, a manager would have it easy. The manager wouldn't need to care who pitched first, second, or third. The manager could pick any combination at random.

In real life, though, the game depends on who is pitching, who is warming up, and who is on the bench waiting to pitch.

The manager or pitching coach needs to consider all the possible combinations and permutations for the pitchers.

Here's how to figure a pitching order:

1. Assign a letter or number to each pitcher:

    #1 for Sandy

    #2 for Roger

    #3 for Lefty

2. Put the three numbers into a chart or grid. The grid will show you the possible combinations as long as you don't care who pitches first, second, or third.

#1	#2	#3
#1	#3	#2
#2	#3	#1
#2	#1	#3
#3	#1	#2
#3	#2	#1

3. Use the grid to write out six possible pitching orders.

IT'S LIKE CRACKING A CODE. YOU CAN SEE ALL THE ARRANGEMENTS AND REARRANGEMENTS, COMBINATIONS AND PERMUTATIONS, FOR YOUR PITCHERS. THEN YOU CAN GO ON TO PICK THE BEST LINEUP.

DECIDE ON A BASEBALL LINEUP

A baseball team has nine players. Your job is to line them up for their turns at bat.

If you can get the players in the right order, you'll help win the game.

Here's how to figure out the right order:

1. Figure out the ways you can line up nine players. Assign a number, 1 through 9, to each of the players, something like this:

   1 — Pitcher

   2 — Catcher

   3 — First base

   4 — Second base

   5 — Third base

   6 — Shortstop

   7 — Left field

   8 — Center field

   9 — Right field

2. Now make a decision about the strength of the hitters. A major league manager might line up hitters (and designated hitters) like this:

   1 — A fast runner

   2 — A good hitter

   3 — The best hitter

   4 — The best power hitter

   5 — The next-best power hitter

   6 — Medium hitter

   7 — Medium hitter

   8 — Next to weakest hitter

   9 — Weakest hitter

Arrange your players in the line-up you think might be best.

3. If you wish, consider changing lineups so a hitter with good potential can get more at-bats.

   If you're looking ahead to a large number of games, though, you may decide you don't need to worry about giving players equal turns. Over the course of a major league season, the best hitters don't come to the plate too many times more than the weakest hitters.

4. If you'd like to see all the possible lineups for your nine players, get out your calculator.

   Think about your lineup this way. When you select your first hitter or designated hitter, you're selecting one out of nine. When you select the next hitter, you're selecting one out of the eight left. Then you're selecting one from the seven left.

   By the time you get to the last of the nine players, you're selecting one out of one left. (Does this remind you of Roger, Sandy, and Lefty? It's the same idea, only this time you have nine players.)

. . . .
DECIDE ON A BASEBALL LINEUP
continued

Here's how to figure all the possible lineups on your calculator:

$$9 \times 8 \times 7 \times 6 \times 5 \times 4 \times 3 \times 2 \times 1 = \square.$$

If you have a scientific calculator, a function key will do all this multiplication for you. Press 9. Then press a key marked ! or x! or n! or nPr.

DO YOU WANT TO TRY FOR ALL THE POSSIBLE LINEUPS OF YOUR NINE PLAYERS? DO YOU LOVE BASEBALL ENOUGH TO PLAY THAT MANY GAMES?

MEASURE YOUR OWN PERSONAL STRIKE ZONE

Baseball and softball players depend on seeing something that is invisible. That's the strike zone, the cube of empty space in front of the hitter at bat.

Step up to the plate, and imagine the ball slicing through the air in front of you.

If the ball angles just right through that empty air, you hope for a good solid hit. You can picture a home run.

If the ball slices away from that empty air, though, you ought to stand still. If you reach too far with your bat, you'll just get a popup or some other weak hit.

Imagine your own personal strike zone hanging in front of you like an invisible rectangle.

Here's how to measure your own personal strike zone:

1. Measure from the ground to your knees. That's the bottom of the strike zone rectangle.

2. Measure from the top of your knees to your chest, or just about the middle of the number on the shirt of your uniform. That's the length of the rectangle, top to bottom.

3. At a baseball diamond, measure the width of home plate. Add two or three inches (5 to 8 centimeters) to this measurement to find the width of your strike zone.

TRY DRAWING THE STRIKE ZONE RECTANGLE SO THAT YOU CAN IMAGINE IT CLEARLY. YOU'LL BE GLAD WHEN THE BALL IS SPEEDING TOWARD YOU AND YOU FIND YOURSELF WITH JUST A SPLIT SECOND TO FIGURE IT ALL OUT.

· · · · · · · · · ·
FIGURE BASEBALL BATTING AVERAGES
· ·

Baseball batting averages are one place where you pronounce numbers as if the decimal points were invisible.

Suppose you step up to the plate for the first time this season, and you hit a home run. Instantly, you have a batting "average" of 1.000. It's not really an average since you have no other numbers to compare. For a while, though, your statistics would look perfect.

Your admirers would ignore the decimal point and say you were "batting one thousand."

(In some sports, you would talk about percentages instead of averages. Then, if your score was perfect, your percentage would be 100%.)

The all-time best major league hitters have had batting averages above .400. A strong major league hitter might hit .300. Ignore the decimal point, and call those averages four hundred and three hundred.

(As percentages, they're 40% and 30%.)

A poor player might joke about getting his batting average higher than his weight. If his weight was between 150 and 200 pounds, for instance, he would joke about a batting average between .150 and .200 (between 15% and 30%).

Here's how to figure batting averages for baseball or softball:

1. Keep count of the number of times the hitter came to bat.

2. Keep track of the number of hits.

3. Divide the number of hits by the number of times the hitter came to bat.

4. Remember that getting a walk doesn't count as a time at bat.

For example, suppose that in the last game the hitter came to bat three times and got one hit.

$$1 \div 2 = \square.$$

Over a season, suppose the hitter came to bat 59 times and got 29 hits.

$$29 \div 59 = \square.$$

REALLY GOOD LITTLE LEAGUE PLAYERS CAN KEEP BATTING AVERAGES THAT NO ONE EVER SEES IN THE MAJOR LEAGUES. SOMETIMES LITTLE LEAGUE AVERAGES GO AS HIGH AS .600 OR .800.

KEEP TRACK OF EARNED RUN AVERAGES

You might want a high batting average in baseball. If you're a pitcher, though, what you don't want is a high earned run average.

Perhaps a pitcher is not pitching well. The hitters hit well, and they get on base from hits or from walks. Then they score.

Each of these scores is an earned run.

An unearned run is something else. No one counts it against the pitcher. Perhaps a shortstop fumbles the ball. Perhaps an outfielder can't catch the ball and allows a batter to get on base and later to score.

Here's how to figure an earned run average:

1. Keep track of the number of earned runs per inning for one pitcher. You might keep track for a few innings, a few games, or a whole season.

2. Divide the number of earned runs by the number of innings. For example, suppose you kept track for three games. During that time, your favorite pitcher pitched a total of 13 innings and gave up 5 earned runs. Divide the 5 earned runs by 13 innings.

$$5 \div 13 = \square.$$

The answer gives you the average earned runs per inning.

3. Now multiply by 9. You need the number of earned runs per 9 innings, even if the pitcher did not pitch 9 innings and even if you didn't keep track for 9 innings.

$$(5 \div 13) \times 9 = \square.$$

NOW YOU CAN FIGURE EARNED RUN AVERAGES FOR ALL YOUR FAVORITE PITCHERS.

· · · · · · · · · ·

KEEP BASKETBALL STATS

· ·

You might like to keep basketball statistics for yourself or your favorite players.

Here's how to figure basketball stats:

1. Count the number of baskets you make during a game or during a season (not the number of points).

2. Keep track of the number of times you tried for a basket.

3. Divide the number of baskets by the number of tries. Suppose you scored 9 baskets out of 15 tries. Divide like this:

   $9 \div 15 = \square$.

4. To get the percentage, multiply that answer by 100.

YOU CAN COUNT YOUR FREE THROWS AT PRACTICE OR DURING A GAME. KEEP TRACK OF THOSE AVERAGES, TOO.

PREDICT YOUR SPORTS FUTURE

Keep statistics, and you can predict your sports future—at least sometimes.

Here's what you need to know:

1. Your win-loss record so far
2. Your win-loss record against a particular opponent
3. The win-loss records of your opponents

   If you win against weak players, you're not proving how well you can do. If you lose to strong players, you still may be playing very well. You need to know how well you perform against opponents whose ability is similar to yours.

   You may see power ratings of this sort used to match opponents in tournaments for several different sports.

4. The changes and trends for yourself or your team

   Perhaps your best teammate just went on to another school. Perhaps you are growing better every day. Surprises are part of the fun of sports.

OF COURSE, SPORTS WOULDN'T BE FUN IF YOU COULD ALWAYS PREDICT WINS AND LOSSES. YOU MAY DO A LOT BETTER THAN YOUR STATISTICS SAY YOU CAN.

GO ON A WINNING STREAK

What do you do if you keep losing but you don't know why? You're playing well. Your team is working hard. You just seem to lose for no particular reason.

The reason might be pure chance.

Here's how to figure it:

1. Try flipping a coin. The coin comes up heads or tails by pure chance.
2. Suppose you've lost four games in a row for no particular reason. Flip until the coin comes up tails four times in a row. That's for no particular reason, too. It just happens.
3. Keep flipping. The coin may come up tails several times in a row, but it's very unlikely that it will come up tails 40 times in a row.

A LOSING STREAK SOMETIMES BEGINS FOR NO PARTICULAR REASON AND SOMETIMES ENDS FOR NO PARTICULAR REASON. YOU MAY BE BACK TO WINNING BEFORE YOU KNOW IT. THERE'S HOPE.

PLAY AN INTERPLANETARY GAME

The people of planet Truth always tell the truth. No one ever lies.

The people of planet Fake never tell the truth. Everyone lies all the time.

Perhaps Ryan is a Truth Person of planet Truth who invents a spaceship and flies out to visit planet Fake.

Or perhaps Kris is a Fake Person of planet Fake who invents a spaceship and flies out to visit planet Truth.

Or maybe neither of these statements is true.

Here are clues to help you figure out who did what:

1. Ryan says he is a Truth Person from planet Truth.

2. Kris says Ryan is a Fake Person from planet Fake.

3. Ryan says that he rode on the spaceship to visit the other planet and make new friends.

4. Kris says she rode on the spaceship to visit the other planet and make new friends.

5. As she stepped off the spaceship, Kris says her first words to Ryan were: "Hello. I'm here to be your friend."

6. As he stepped off the spaceship, Ryan says his first words to Kris were: "Goodbye. I don't want to be your friend."

7. Ryan says he and Kris are friends.

8. Kris says she likes space travel. Some day soon she hopes to visit planet Earth.

Look for statements that cannot both be true at the same time. Look for a statement that contradicts another statement.

Sometimes you'll find a statement that is of no use or that just repeats another statement. Make sure you don't get confused.

SEE IF YOU CAN INVENT YOUR OWN TRUTH TELLING GAME.

PUZZLE OVER PETS AND PEOPLE

People love pets, and pets love people.
See if you can match four people with their pets.

Here's the story:

Buffy, Duffy, Rickie, and Danny
each have a pet. The pets are
named Fluffy, Spot, Mickey, and
Vickie. The pets are a cat, a dog, a
mouse, and a parakeet.

Here are clues to help you match the people, the pets, and the names of the pets:

1. No person's name rhymes with the name of his or her pet.
2. No person's name begins with the same letter as the name of his or her pet.

	DOG	MOUSE	PARAKEET	CAT	FLUFFY	SPOT	MICKEY	VICKIE
BUFFY								
DUFFY								
RICKIE								
DANNY								
FLUFFY								
SPOT								
MICKEY								
VICKIE								

PUZZLE OVER PETS AND PEOPLE
continued

3. Mickey is not a mouse, and Fluffy is not a cat.

4. Danny's pet is neither a mouse nor a parakeet.

5. The pets with rhyming names are not parakeets, and neither of them belongs to Duffy.

6. The parakeet does not belong to either of the people with rhyming names.

7. Mickey does not belong to Buffy.

Make a chart or grid to help you make the matches.

As soon as you find one match, you can cross out other possibilities. For instance, if pet #1 turns out to be a mouse, then pet #1 cannot be a dog, cat, or parakeet. Use logic to find the matches.

PERHAPS YOU CAN DESIGN YOUR OWN LOGIC PUZZLE.

ANSWERS FOR SECTION 14: PLAY THE WORLD'S BEST GAMES

Make Your Calculator Talk:

1. 505 = SOS
2. 8075 = SLOB
3. 3373 = ELSE
4. 3507 = LOSE
5. 7718 = BILL
6. 345 = SHE
7. 8078 = BLOB
8. 0.7734 = HELLO
9. 77345 = SHELL
10. 5376606 = GOGGLES

Select an All-Star Pitching Staff:

Step 3.   Sandy, Roger, Lefty
Sandy, Lefty, Roger
Roger, Lefty, Sandy
Roger, Sandy, Lefty
Lefty, Sandy, Roger
Lefty, Roger, Sandy

Decide on a Baseball Lineup:

Step 4. $9 \times 8 \times 7 \times 6 \times 5 \times 4 \times 3 \times 2 \times 1 = 362{,}880$ possible lineups

Figure Baseball Batting Averages:

Example: $1 \div 2 = .500$
$29 \div 59 = .491$ (That's 50% or 49.1%.)

Keep Track of Earned Run Averages:

Step 2. $5 \div 13 = 0.38$ average ER per inning
Step 3. $5 \div 13 \times 9 = 3.46$ ER average for nine innings

Keep Basketball Stats:

Step 3. $9 \div 15 = 0.60$ average
Step 4. $0.60 \times 100 = 60\%$ average

Play an Interplanetary Game

Kris is a Truth Person from planet Truth. She rode on the spaceship to visit planet Fake. Ryan is a Fake Person from planet Fake. Ryan does not own a spaceship.

Notice that Ryan's statements cannot all be true at the same time. Ryan says he wants to make new friends (#3) and that he has made a new friend (Kris)(#7). Yet he also says that he does not want to be friends with Kris (#6).

Look at the statements Kris makes. You can see that she is telling the truth because all of her statements can be true at the same time.

. . . .

ANSWERS FOR SECTION 14: PLAY THE WORLD'S BEST GAMES

continued

Puzzle Over Pets and People:

Buffy's pet is a dog named Vickie.

Duffy's pet is a mouse named Spot.

Rickie's pet is a parakeet named Fluffy.

Danny's pet is a cat named Mickey.

Follow the clues about the pets and people like this:

1. If no person's name rhymes with the name of his or her pet. Then you know that Fluffy does not belong to Buffy or Duffy. You also can tell that neither Mickey nor Vickie belongs to Rickie. Make X marks on the grid by each name.

2. If no person's name begins with the same letter as his or her pet, then you know that neither Danny nor Duffy has a dog.

3. If Mickey is not a mouse and Fluffy is not a cat, mark X on the grid by those spots.

4. Danny's pet is neither a mouse nor a parakeet. You already know from clue #2 that Danny's pet is not a dog. There's only one pet left. Danny's pet must be a cat.

If Danny has a cat, then the other people, Buffy, Duffy, and Rickie, do not have a cat. You can X out those spots on the grid.

5. If the pets with rhyming names are not parakeets, then neither Mickey nor Vickie is a parakeet. Mickey and Vickie also do not belong to Duffy. Look at the X marks on your grid. Spot is the only pet name left for Duffy. Spot must belong to Duffy. Now you also know that Spot does not belong to Buffy, Rickie, or Danny.

6. The parakeet does not belong to either of the people with rhyming names. Therefore, the parakeet does not belong to Buffy or Duffy. Mark your grid.

7. Make an X to show that Mickey does not belong to Buffy.

As the grid fills with X marks. you can make the rest of the connections between pets and people.

15. MAKE MAGIC WITH SQUARES

*B*enjamin Franklin loved magic squares. He liked to sit by himself sometimes and make magic squares for fun.

He told his friends that he had developed a knack for magic squares. He could fill in the spaces as fast as he could write down the numbers.

Benjamin Franklin was not alone in his love for this sort of puzzle. The idea of magic squares is thousands of years old.

The mystery is that many ancient peoples seem to have discovered magic squares on their own. People might live across the world from one another, with no way to communicate. Yet people in different lands would all be experimenting with the same sort of ideas about magic squares.

You can experiment with magic squares, too.

Perhaps you'll love them as much as Benjamin Franklin did.

SOLVE A MAGIC DRAGON PUZZLE

Thousands of years ago, the story goes, Emperor Fu-hsi of China was walking along a beach beside a river.

The emperor came upon magic footprints in the sand. He knew at once that they were the footprints of a divine dragon horse and that they contained a message from heaven.

First, the emperor had to solve the puzzle of the numbers on the footprints. Here's how the magic footprints looked:

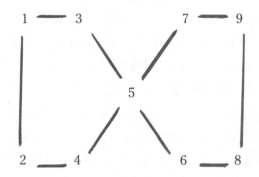

Here's how to add up the message of the footprints:

1. Add all the even numbers.

2. Add all the odd numbers, but leave out the number 5 since it is in the middle between the other numbers. (If you put the numbers in a straight line, you'll find that 5 is still in the middle.)

You ought to arrive at the same total for the even and the odd numbers. If you need help, see the answer at the end of this section.

THE MAGIC FOOTPRINTS SHOW THE ANCIENT IDEA OF YIN AND YANG. THE EVEN NUMBERS ADD UP TO THE SAME TOTAL AS THE ODD NUMBERS. THEY ARE IN BALANCE. THE MESSAGE IS: KEEP ALL THINGS IN BALANCE AND GOOD ORDER.

· · · · · · · · · ·

A TURTLE STORY

· ·

Hundreds of years passed in China. The new emperor, Emperor Yu, was worried about his people. He was not sure he would be a good ruler.

The story is that he, too, walked along the river's edge in search of inspiration.

As he neared the end of his walk, a turtle crawled slowly out of the river. The turtle carried a design on its back, the design of a magic square. The emperor knew at once that the puzzle held the answer to his problem.

The ancient people of China copied the turtle's design by making designs with strings. They tied knots and arranged the strings in squares.

They used white string for odd numbers and red string for even numbers.

The home of the divine turtle was the River Loh. The name for the ancient magic square is Loh Shu.

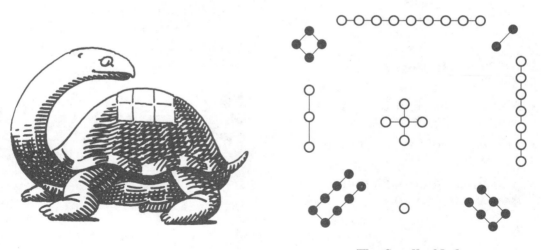

The Scroll of Loh

: SEE WHETHER YOU CAN ATTACH THE RIGHT NUMBERS TO THE STRINGS. THEN
: GO ON TO SEE HOW TO WORK THE PUZZLE OF THE TURTLE'S DESIGN.
: PERHAPS YOU WILL FIND THE SECRET OF THE MAGIC TURTLE.

MAKE A LITTLE MAGIC WITH A SMALL SQUARE

Draw a small magic square, and then use it to puzzle your friends. In the story from ancient China, the magic turtle that crawled from the River Loh carried this design, the same magic square, on its back.

This magic square is 3 × 3. It has space for only nine numbers.

Here is one way to arrange a small magic square:

4	9	2
3	5	7
8	1	6

Here's how to play with the numbers:

1. Add each row left to right (or right to left).
2. Add each column up and down (or down and up).
3. Add the numbers diagonally, from corner to corner.

Perhaps you see what is magic about magic squares. They are puzzles in which the numbers always add up to the same total.

Here's how to puzzle your friends:

1. Draw a magic square, and leave out one or more of the numbers.
2. Give your friends a clue. Say, "There's something special about the number 15, but 15 is not one of the missing numbers."

NOW GO ON TO MAKE YOUR OWN MAGIC SQUARES AND TO CREATE BIGGER AND BETTER PUZZLES.

MAKE YOUR OWN ODD-NUMBERED MAGIC

Perhaps you would like to puzzle over puzzles. See how many 3 × 3 magic squares you can make for yourself.

Here's how to make your own 3 × 3 magic squares:

1. Draw a 3 × 3 magic square with nine spaces for numbers.

2. Write the numbers 1 through 9 in a straight line like this:

   1 2 3 4 5 6 7 8 9

3. Place the number that falls in the exact middle of your lineup, number 5, in the center space of your magic square.

4. Decide where to place the first number of your lineup, number 1. You can put it in any space in the magic square except the center space.

5. Place the last number of your lineup, number 9, in the space diametrically opposite to the space where you put number 1.

6. Now fill in other spaces with the remaining numbers of your line-up. Fill them in so that each row (left to right), each column (up and down), and each diagonal (corner to corner) adds up to the same total, 15.

: **IF YOU KEEP WORKING, YOU'LL FIND**
: **EIGHT POSSIBLE WAYS TO FILL IN**
: **THE SPACES.**

BRANCH OUT TO MORE ODD-NUMBERED MAGIC

You can make your 3 × 3 squares even more puzzling.

Here's how to make fancy 3 × 3 magic squares:

1. Draw a 3 × 3 magic square with nine spaces for numbers.

2. Write a line of 9 numbers. This time, though, don't just write 1 to 9. Write a complicated series.

   You could write by 2's, like this:

    2 4 6 8 10 12 14 16 18

   You could write by 3's, like this:

    3 6 9 12 15 18 21 24 27

   You could use fractions. You could use big numbers. You could think up your own series of numbers. The series has to follow a regular sequence, though. It has to make sense.

3. Choose the number that falls in the exact middle of your lineup. For example, if you are writing by 2's as in step 2, you'll find the number 10 in the middle of the lineup.

4. Place that middle number in the center space of your magic square.

BRANCH OUT TO MORE ODD-NUMBERED MAGIC
continued

5. Decide where to place the first number of your lineup. You can put it in any space on the magic square except the center space. For example:

?	2	?
?	10	?
?	?	?

6. Place the last number of your lineup in the space diametrically opposite the first number. For example:

?	2	?
?	10	?
?	18	?

7. Add the row you have now. For example: 2 + 10 + 18 = ☐.

8. Fill in the other spaces so that they add up to the same answer. For example:

16	2	12
6	10	14
8	18	4

CHECK THAT ALL THE ROWS, COLUMNS, AND DIAGONALS ADD UP TO THE SAME TOTAL, LEFT AND RIGHT, UP AND DOWN, CORNER TO CORNER. YOU CAN GO ON TO MAKE YOUR MAGIC SQUARES MORE AND MORE PUZZLING.

········
CONSTRUCT PERFECT MAGIC
·······························

Draw this perfect 5 × 5 square:

1	24	17	15	8
14	7	5	23	16
22	20	13	6	4
10	3	21	19	12
18	11	9	2	25

Then use it to make a puzzle for your friends.

Why is this square perfect? It's perfect because it adds up to the same total every which way—just perfectly.

Here's one way to play with the numbers:

1. Add each row of numbers left and right. Use a calculator if you wish.
2. Add each column of numbers up and down.
3. Add the numbers diagonally, from corner to corner.

   You'll see they all add up perfectly—to the same total.

Here's how to puzzle your friends:

1. Draw the 5 × 5 magic square, and leave out one or more of the numbers.
2. Give your friends a clue. Say, "There's something special about the number 65, but 65 is not one of the missing numbers."

YOU COULD MAKE BIGGER AND BIGGER MAGIC SQUARES. IF YOU COULD MAKE A 7 × 7 SQUARE, YOU MUST MAKE ALL THE ROWS ADD UP TO 369. PEOPLE HAVE EVEN EXPERIMENTED WITH A CALENDAR MAGIC SQUARE OF 365 SPACES, ONE FOR EACH DAY OF THE YEAR.

· · · · · · · · · · ·
COLOR PERFECT MAGIC

· ·

Use your perfect magic squares to make magic with colors. Colors are one more way to make magic square numbers add up perfectly.

You'll need three different colors for a 5 × 5 magic square. Use highlighters, or else circle the numbers with markers, coloring pens, or crayons.

Try coloring the CONSTRUCT PERFECT MAGIC square on page 286.

Here's how to color the numbers:

1. Color the center number, 13.

2. Use a second color for the inner square of numbers (7, 5, 23, 20, 6, 3, 21, 19).

3. Use a third color for the numbers in the outer square.

Here's how to add up the colors:

1. Add any two numbers that are the same color and are across from each other. The two numbers must be an equal distance from the center space. For example:

$$5 + 21 = \square$$
$$12 + 14 = \square$$

2. Figure out the number of small squares inside the large square. Then add 1.

$$5 \times 5 + 1 = \square$$

You should be seeing that same magic number.

⋮ **GO ON TO MAKE EVEN MORE**
⋮ **CONNECTIONS**

········

CONNECT PERFECT MAGIC

··································

Magic squares can show you even more connections.

Here's what you need:

A magic square
A highlighter or pencil
A ruler or straightedge

Here's how to connect a pattern of magic square numbers:

1. Use the highlighter or pencil to connect a string of numbers on the magic square. Place the ruler or straightedge so you can draw a straight line from the center of one small square to another.

2. For example, in the magic square below, draw a line that connects numbers 1, 2, 3, 4, and 5. Then draw a line to connect 21, 22, 23, 24, and 25.

1	24	17	15	8
14	7	5	23	16
22	20	13	6	4
10	3	21	19	12
18	11	9	2	25

YOU'LL SEE BALANCE AND SYMMETRY INSIDE EVERY MAGIC SQUARE. IT'S ALMOST LIKE MATH MUSIC.

....
MAKE A MAGIC TUBE
....

You can make a tube that shows you magic-square numbers. As you build bigger and bigger magic squares, the tube can make choosing the numbers quick and easy.

Here's what you need:

Graph paper or plain paper

A pencil

A ruler

A piece of clear flexible plastic (Heavy-duty vinyl, the sort used for notebook dividers, is best.)

A permanent-ink pen for writing on plastic

Paper clips

Here's how to make your magic tube:

1. With the pencil, draw a 5 × 5 magic square on the paper, along with the pyramids of numbers as shown in the diagram.

Make the spaces at least ³/4 inch (2 centimeters) across. Draw the lines and numbers extra dark so that you can trace them onto the plastic.

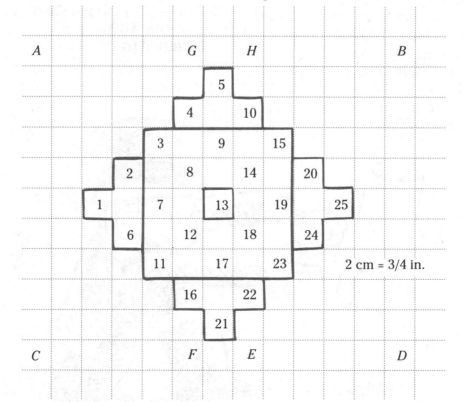

A Grid for Creating a 5 × 5 Magic Square

MAKE A MAGIC TUBE
continued

Stop to see how the numbers move up the pyramids in order. For instance, look at 1, 2, 3, 4, 5, and 21, 22, 23, 24, 25.

2. Carefully trace the square and the numbers onto the clear plastic, using the permanent-ink pen.

3. Roll the plastic into a tube. Roll the *AC* edge up to the *EH* line in the middle of the square. Secure the tube with the paper clips.

   If you turn the tube slightly each way, you will be able to see six numbers in the blank spaces next to the center number. Write the numbers in the empty spaces on the original paper square.

4. Unroll the tube, and roll it up the other way. Roll the *BD* edge up to the *GF* line in the middle of the tube. Secure the tube with the paper clips.

If you turn the tube slightly each way, you will be able to see six numbers in the blank spaces next to the center number. Write the numbers in the empty spaces on the original paper square.

5. Now look at the paper square. You can add up the numbers in any direction, left to right, up and down, corner to corner. Each time, you should find the same magic number as the total.

LOOK AT HOW THE NUMBERS ON THE TUBE MOVE IN ORDER. YOU CAN USE A PYRAMID OF NUMBERS LIKE THIS TO MAKE BIGGER AND BIGGER MAGIC SQUARES

· · · · · · · · · ·
MAKE EVEN-NUMBERED MAGIC
· ·

You can also make even-numbered magic squares. They're a bit different from the odd-numbered squares you made earlier.

A 4 × 4 magic square has spaces for 16 numbers.

Here's how to draw one kind of 4 × 4 magic square:

1. Draw a 4 × 4 square, and write in the numbers in order. Begin at the upper left corner with the number 1, and finish in the lower right corner with the number 16.

   Here's how your square should look:

1	2	3	4
5	6	7	8
9	10	11	12
13	14	15	16

2. Work a little beginning magic on your square. Add the opposite corners. For example:

   $$1 + 16 = \square$$
   $$13 + 4 = \square$$

   Figure out the number of small squares in the big square, and then add 1:

   $$4 \times 4 + 1 = \square$$

   Then add the largest number on the square plus the smallest number:

   $$16 + 1 = \square$$

   You should be seeing the same magic number.

Here's how to make a puzzle out of your 4 × 4 square:

1. Draw a blank 4 × 4 square. Fill in the corner numbers and the four center numbers. (In other words, you'll still have the same numbers in the two diagonal lines.)

   Your square should look like this:

1	?	?	4
?	6	7	?
?	10	11	?
13	?	?	16

2. You have eight numbers left over (2, 3, 5, 8, 9, 12, 14, and 15). Exchange each number for one other.

   Here's the rule: The two numbers you exchange must add up to 17. For example, 2 + 15 = 17, so let the 2 and the 15 change places in the new square.

   Figure out how to switch each of the other numbers.

3. When you're finished switching the numbers, add up the numbers to see whether you're right. Each row, up and down, right and left, corner to corner, should add up to 34.

. . . .
MAKE EVEN-NUMBERED MAGIC
continued

BENJAMIN FRANKLIN ESPECIALLY LIKED EVEN-NUMBERED MAGIC SQUARES. HE SAID THAT HIS 16 × 16 MAGIC SQUARE WAS "THE MOST MAGICALLY MAGICAL OF ANY MAGIC SQUARE EVER MADE BY ANY MAGICIAN."

SOLVE AN ANGEL'S PUZZLE

Almost 500 years ago, Albrecht Dürer engraved a picture that he called *Melancholia*. The woodcut shows a melancholy angel, silent and brooding. The angel is so sad that she has tossed away her work and her tools. They lie scattered all around her.

The sad angel is even neglecting a magic square that hangs on her wall.

You can solve the puzzle of the angel's magic square. See whether you can fill in the missing numbers:

?	3	2	13
5	?	11	8
9	6	?	12
4	15	14	?

Hint: Each row of numbers must add up to 34. The numbers must be in the sequence 1 through 16, and you can't repeat any of the numbers.

THE MAGIC SQUARE SHOWN IN DURER'S WOODCUT IS A MYSTERY. WHY DOES THE ANGEL KEEP IT IN HER WORKROOM? WHY IS THE ANGEL SO SAD? ALTHOUGH MAGIC SQUARES ARE THOUSANDS OF YEARS OLD, THE MAGIC SQUARE OF THE WOODCUT IS THE FIRST EUROPEAN MAGIC SQUARE THAT ANYONE KNOWS ABOUT. THAT'S A MYSTERY, TOO.

MAKE AN ALPHABET SQUARE

You'll never run out of numbers for your magic squares. In case you need a change, though, you can forget numbers and make a magic square with the letters of the alphabet.

Just replace numbers with letters. This is like working with an alphabet code. You number the letters of the alphabet: 1 for A, 2 for B, 3 for C, and 4 for D. (You can keep going if you want a bigger alphabet square.)

You can even try the letters of your own name.

Here are three ways to mark the same magic square:

A	D	B	C
B	C	A	D
C	B	D	A
D	A	C	B

1	4	2	3
2	3	1	4
3	2	4	1
4	1	3	2

M	Y	A	R
A	R	M	Y
R	A	Y	M
Y	M	R	A

AS YOU FIGURE OUT BIGGER AND BIGGER MAGIC SQUARES, YOU CAN WRITE IN LONGER NAMES AND MESSAGES. YOU'LL FEEL AS THOUGH YOU HAVE A SECRET CODE.

ANSWERS FOR SECTION 15: MAKE MAGIC WITH SQUARES

Solve a Magic Dragon Puzzle:

Step 1. $2 + 4 + 6 + 8 = 20$
Step 2. $1 + 3 + 7 + 9 = 20$

Make a Little Magic with a Small Square:

Step 1. $4 + 9 + 2 = 15$
$3 + 5 + 7 = 15$
$8 + 1 + 6 = 15$
Step 2. $4 + 3 + 8 = 15$
$9 + 5 + 1 = 15$
$2 + 7 + 6 = 15$
Step 3. $4 + 5 + 6 = 15$
$8 + 5 + 2 = 15$

Branch Out to More Odd-Numbered Magic:

Step 7. $2 + 10 + 18 = 30$
Step 8. $16 + 2 + 12 = 30$
$6 + 10 + 14 = 30$
$8 + 18 + 4 = 30$
$16 + 10 + 4 = 30$
$8 + 10 + 12 = 30$

Construct Perfect Magic

Step 1. $1 + 24 + 17 + 15 + 8 = 65$
$14 + 7 + 5 + 23 + 16 = 65$
$22 + 20 + 13 + 6 + 4 = 65$
$10 + 3 + 21 + 19 + 12 = 65$
$18 + 11 + 9 + 2 + 25 = 65$

Step 2. $1 + 14 + 22 + 10 + 18 = 65$
$24 + 7 + 20 + 3 + 11 = 65$
$17 + 5 + 13 + 21 + 9 = 65$
$15 + 23 + 6 + 19 + 2 = 65$
$8 + 16 + 4 + 12 + 25 = 65$

Step 3. $1 + 7 + 13 + 19 + 25 = 65$
$18 + 3 + 13 + 23 + 8 = 65$

Color Perfect Magic:

Step 1. $5 + 21 = 26$
$12 + 14 = 26$

Step 2. $5 \times 5 + 1 = 26$

Make Even-Numbered Magic:

Step 2. $1 + 16 = 17$
$13 + 4 = 17$
$4 \times 4 + 1 = 17$
$16 + 1 = 17$

Step 3.   Switch the numbers, and you ought to finish a 4×4 square like this:

1	15	14	4
12	6	7	9
8	10	11	5
13	3	2	15

Solve an Angel's Puzzle:

Here's the angel's magic square, with the missing numbers filled in:

16	3	2	13
5	10	11	8
9	6	7	12
4	15	14	1

16. THROW A MATH PARTY

*F*or your next special occasion, think of throwing a math party.

Would you like to serve combinations and permutations of party food? Would you like to shape a party cake? Would you like to take your friends on a treasure hunt? Would you like to cut paper up into magic strips?

Send the invitations—in secret code, of course—and get going on the best party ever.

· · · · · · · · · ·
PLAN COMBINATIONS AND PERMUTATIONS OF PARTY FOOD
· ·

In any party, the focus is on food. In planning your math party, then, first plan the food.

Balance is important in planning food, just as it is in math.

Here's a good menu:

Straight 8 Cucumbers
Green Pepper Flowers Fibonacci
Radish Rose Centers
Carrot Curls
Parsley or Coriander Leaves
with 1,2,3 Dip

Make Your Own Combinations and
Permutations Sandwiches
with
Ham, Turkey, Cheeses, Hummus,
Mayonnaise, Tomatoes,
Onions, Lettuce, Pickles,
Mustard, Relish
(How many combinations can
you make?)

A Numbers Birthday Cake

Make Your Own Ice Cream
Combinations and Permutations
with
Vanilla, Chocolate, Strawberry
Ice Cream,
Chocolate Syrup, Fruit Syrup,
Butterscotch Syrup,
Marshmallow Syrup, Peanuts, Walnuts,
Chocolate Sprinkles, Mixed Sprinkles
(How many combinations can you
make?)

1,2,3,5 Punch

LOOK FOR RECIPES FOR STRAIGHT 8 CUCUMBERS, GREEN PEPPER FLOWERS FIBONACCI, RADISH ROSES, CARROT CURLS, THE DIP, THE PUNCH, AND, OF COURSE, A VERY SPECIAL BIRTHDAY CAKE.

FIX A FANCY SHAPES PARTY PLATTER

Arrange a platter of very shapely vegetables. Then fix 1,2,3 Dip to go with them.

Straight 8 Cucumbers:

Plan one-half cucumber for each person. Wash the cucumbers thoroughly. Use the tines of a fork to mark each cucumber from stem end down. Cut each cucumber in half lengthwise. Cut each half in half again, lengthwise. Then cut each quarter in half lengthwise. Your cucumber is now in eighths, and ready to go on the party platter.

Green Pepper Flowers Fibonacci:

Plan one-half green pepper per person. Wash the green peppers. Slice them crosswise, and arrange the circles on the platter.

Radish Rose Centers:

Make each rose by cutting five petal slices from the tip end of the radish toward the stem end. Leave the slices attached to the stem end. Inside these slices, cut three more slices. Place the radish roses in ice water.

When it's time for the party, place a radish rose in the center of each slice of green pepper.

Caution: You need adult help using a knife and peeler.

Carrot Curls:

Scrub and peel carrots. With a peeler, cut long, thin ribbons of carrot. Work from the stem end toward the root tip. Place the carrot ribbons in ice water to make them curl.

PLACE SPRIGS OF PARSLEY AND CORIANDER ON THE PLATTER AMONG THE GREEN PEPPERS AND CARROT CURLS.

· · · · · · · · · · ·
1, 2, 3 DIP
· ·

The dip for your fancy-shaped vegetables is as easy as mixing one, two, three:

> 1 part mustard
> 2 parts mayonnaise
> 3 parts yogurt

If you wish, season the mixture with garlic powder, salt, pepper, and other spices or herbs that you like.

YOUR SHAPELY APPETIZERS ARE ALL READY FOR DIPPING AND EATING.

SHAPE A NUMBERS BIRTHDAY CAKE

Here's how to make a cake shaped in the right numbers for a birthday or other special occasion.

You can use your own favorite cake recipe. (One cake recipe makes one number. If you want to put together two numbers, double the original recipe.)

Decide the number or numbers you want, and then bake the cake like this:

- For the number 8, bake the cake in two 9-inch round pans.
- For the number 9, bake the cake in one 9-inch round pan and one 9-inch square pan.
- For the other numbers, bake the cake in one large $9^1/_2 \times 13$-inch pan.

Cut away part shown in white. (You'll have a few leftover cake bits.) Then outline the numbers with icing, and decorate them.

Birthday Cake Numbers

THIS CAN SHAPE UP TO BE A VERY SPECIAL NUMBERS CAKE.

MIX UP 1, 2, 3, 5 PUNCH

You can remember what you need for this punch by the numbers:

> 1 quart ginger ale
> 2 quarts lemonade
> 3 quarts apple juice
> 5 trays of grape juice ice cubes

THEN GIVE YOUR PUNCH EXTRA COLORS. FLOAT FRESH MINT LEAVES ON TOP.

HUNT FOR HIDDEN TREASURE

You can conduct an outside treasure hunt in a yard or a playground or on a beach. You can hunt for indoor treasure inside a whole house or school or inside one room or classroom.

All you need is a stash of suitable treasure and a good map.

Here are some ideas for the treasure:

- A horde of gold-wrapped chocolate coins.
- A reach-in box of prizes.
- Ornaments or decorated eggs for your guests to hang on a tree. (You don't need to wait for Christmas, Easter, or Rosh Hashanah).
- Candles or candy decorations for your guests to put on a birthday cake.
- Snapshots or pictures of the guests—a way of introducing people. Include some facts about each guest.

Here's what you need to make your map:

A directional compass

Graph paper or plain paper

A pencil

A ruler

A clipboard or other way to hold your paper as you walk

Here's how to make the map:

1. Walk around the party location. Choose a starting point. Decide on several places to hide treasures or more clues.

. . . .

HUNT FOR HIDDEN TREASURE
continued

2. Stand at the starting point, and look ahead to the closest treasure or next clue location.

   Use the directional compass to figure out the direction to that first point. On the paper, write the direction for north and the direction to the first point.

   The compass works just as well inside as outside.

3. Pace the distance to the first location, and record the number of paces.

   Hint: A pace is the normal length of your step. Your guests may have different paces, so you may want to write the length of your pace on the map. Or you may need to help your guests a bit with the distance to each location.

4. Decide on a scale for your map. If you are using graph paper, perhaps one pace might equal the length of one or two squares on your map. If you are using plain paper, perhaps one pace might equal ¼ or ½ inch (1 or 2 centimeters).

5. Draw a line on the paper from the starting point to the first location. Make sure the line goes in the right direction. (For example, if the top of the paper is north and the first location is to the northwest, you will need to use your compass to help you angle the line in that direction.)

6. Standing at the first point, look ahead to the second location you've chosen for treasures or clues. Use your compass to find the direction, and pace the distance. Soon you'll have mapped all the treasure locations.

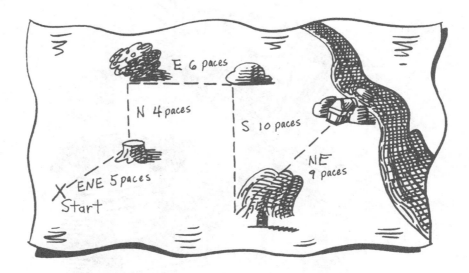

Sample Map

HUNT FOR HIDDEN TREASURE
continued

Hint: *If you want an extra-interesting and creative treasure hunt, draw a map to a first location. At that location, plant a clue or another map. Then have the guests go on to yet another clue or another map. That's how pirates probably hid their treasure.*

You could draw each portion of the map on a separate piece of paper, and hide each new direction at each destination. In this sample, the destinations are the tree stump, elderberry bush, large rock, and willow tree.

The last destination might be the site for the party, perhaps a decorated room or refreshments table, a barbecue grill, or a tree on which to hang eggs or ornaments. Or it might be an especially interesting treasure, with enough for everybody.

IF YOU MAKE A GOOD ENOUGH MAP, EVERYBODY WINS. BUT PIRATES WOULD NOT HAVE WANTED TO MAKE LIFE EASY FOR TREASURE HUNTERS.

FIGURE OUT A COMPASS

Release the needle on the compass. Hold the compass flat until the needle stops moving and points north. Turn the compass until the needle and the mark for north are in line.

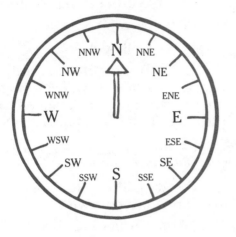

Compass

Now find east, west, and south. Perhaps you can also find directions you don't usually consider, such as NNE (north northeast) and SSW (south southwest).

THE CIRCLE FOR THE COMPASS HAS 360 DEGREES, THE SAME NUMBER OF DEGREES AS IN ALL CIRCLES. IF YOU WANTED TO, YOU COULD FIND 360 DIFFERENT DIRECTIONS.

CUT TRICKY PAPER STRIPS

Show your friends how to cut mysterious strips of paper.

Give your friends paper, scissors, and pencils. Make sure you also have plenty of sturdy tape or glue sticks on hand.

A nineteenth-century German astronomer, Augustus Ferdinand Möbius, invented these tricky strips. Magicians have been happy about them ever since, and so have a lot of other people.

Hint: *If you have several guests and want to make a lot of paper strips, use a roll of adding machine paper available in office-supply stores.*

Here's how to cut Möbius strips:
1. Cut a strip of paper. Give the strip a half-twist, and tape or glue the two ends together.

   You've just made a Möbius strip. If you trace around it with your finger or a pencil, you'll see something surprising.

A Möbius Strip

The surprise is that the strip has only one side and only one edge.

2. Cut out another strip. On this one, draw a line down the center of each side. Then twist, and tape or glue.
   Cut the strip in half along the line you drew. Since you're cutting the strip in half, you might expect to get two strips. See

what you really get.

3. Cut out another strip. On this one, draw a line down each side about a third of the distance from the edge. Twist, and tape or glue.

Hint: *Use extra tape or glue so the strip doesn't come apart as you cut.*

Cut the strip along the lines. You'll need to cut twice around.

One of the results will be a small loop. Try cutting the small loop in half, and see what else happens.

4. Cut out two identical strips. Hold them together, one exactly on top of the other, and twist them together in exactly the same way. Tape or glue the top strip into a loop. Then reach underneath, and tape or glue the bottom strip into a separate loop. The top and bottom strips ought to be nested together but not actually attached.

   Now you have two strips, one inside the other. Put your finger or a pencil between the two, and trace all the way around. You have proved that the strips are separate.

·········
CUT TRICKY PAPER STRIPS
continued

Or are they?

Gently pull apart the double loop, and see what opens up.

If you want a frustrating puzzle, just try to put the two strips back together the way they were before.

5. Again, cut out two identical strips. Draw a line down the center of the top strip. Tape or glue the two strips so the taped loops are nested together.

Cut along the center line you drew on the top strip. By now, you must be used to surprises.

If you want to see the surprises that other people have found as they cut and twisted, look at the end of this section.

SOME TIME WHEN YOU WATCH A MAGICIAN PERFORM, TRY TO SEE HOW THE IDEA OF THE MÖBIUS STRIP WORKS FOR MAGIC TRICKS. SOMETIMES, YOU CAN SEE THE MÖBIUS STRIP IDEA ON FILM AND TAPE RECORDERS OR ON CONVEYOR BELTS IN FACTORIES. THE IDEA IS USEFUL BECAUSE THE TAPES AND BELTS WEAR EVENLY AND DON'T NEED TO BE REPLACED SO OFTEN. YOU MIGHT EVEN SEE A MÖBIUS STRIP ON TELEVISION IN AN OLD SCIENCE FICTION RERUN.

PLAY A GAME OF BLINDFOLD BLUFF

You can play this game indoors or out. You need to pick a starting point and a goal at least 10 feet (about 3 meters) away. The goal can be a ribbon tied on a chair, an upright stick, a tree, or a chalk line on a wall or fence.

Here's what else you need:

A bandanna, heavy handkerchief, or other piece of cloth for a blindfold

A yardstick or tape measure

Paper and pencil

Here's how to play:

1. Tie the bandanna, handkerchief, or other piece of cloth over the eyes of the first player. No peeking!

2. Face the player in a direct line toward the goal.

3. Tell the player to walk straight forward toward the goal.

4. When the player is level with the goal, but on the left or right of it, say, "Stop!"

5. Measure and write down the distance from the player's stopping place to the goal. Note whether

the player has stopped to the right or left of the goal.

6. Continue the game until each player has had a chance. The player who gets closest to the goal wins.

7. Measure each player's bare feet. If you measure carefully, you'll probably find that one foot is very slightly larger than the other.

8. After the game, look at all the measurements. You may find that each player turned away from the goal, left or right, in the direction of his or her shorter foot.

MAYBE YOU CAN FIGURE OUT WHY. LOOK ON PAGE 310 AT THE END OF THIS SECTION IF YOU WANT A POSSIBLE ANSWER.

· · · · · · · · · · ·
PLAY A BIRTHDAY CALCULATOR TRICK
· ·

You can discover your friends' birthdays. Just use your calculator.

Here's how to play the birthday calculator trick:

1. Have a friend enter in the calculator the number of the month in which he or she was born. For example, if the friend was born in April, the fourth month of the year, he or she will enter 4.

   Don't look. You'll know soon enough.

2. Now ask your friend to calculate like this:

   Note: *After each calculation enter the equal sign.*

   • Multiply by 20.
   • Add 3.
   • Multiply by 5.

3. Have the friend add the day of the month. For example, if your friend was born on April 3, he or she will enter +, then 3.

4. Then have your friend calculate again:
   • Multiply by 20.
   • Add 3.
   • Multiply by 5.

5. Get the friend to add the last two digits of the year he or she was born. For example, if the year was 1990, the friend will enter +, then 90.

6. Have the friend subtract 1515.

READ THE DAY, MONTH, AND YEAR OF YOUR FRIEND'S BIRTH.

ANSWERS FOR SECTION 16: THROW A MATH PARTY

Cut Paper Tricks:

Step 2. Instead of two strips, you get one long narrow loop.

Step 3. You get a large loop and a small loop linked together. If you cut the small loop in half, you get another large loop, still linked to the other.

Step 4. You get a single loop, as if the two strips were not separate at all. Your single loop ought to have four half-twists in it.

Step 5. You get two loops linked together.

Play a Game of Blindfold Bluff:

The larger foot covers slightly more distance than the smaller. Therefore, a person may tend to turn slightly in the direction of the smaller foot. A person who was lost in the dark and walking over a long distance might eventually travel in a complete circle in the direction of the smaller foot.

Play a Birthday Calculator Trick:

Step 2. $4 \times 20 = 80$
$80 + 3 = 83$
$83 \times 5 = 415$

Step 3. $415 + 3 = 418$

Step 4. $418 \times 20 = 8360$
$8360 + 3 = 8363$
$8363 \times 5 = 41,815$

Step 5. $41,815 + 90 = 41,905$

Step 6. $41,905 - 1515 = 40390$

MATH SIGNS AND SYMBOLS

+	Plus, add, shows a positive number
−	Minus, subtract, shows a negative number
× or ·	Times, multiply
÷ or /	Divide
=	Equals
≠	Is not equal
≈	Is similar or about equal
>	Is greater than
<	Is less than
∞	Infinity
√	Square root
π	Pi
Φ	Phi

APPENDIX

CONSTRUCT BASIC ANGLES AND SHAPES

1. Use a protractor

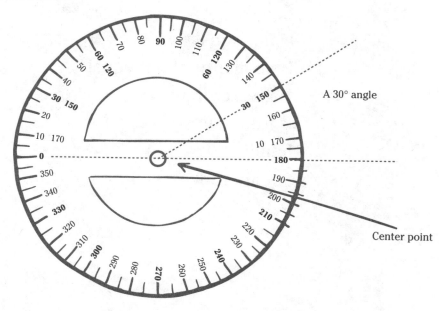

A 30° angle

Center point

A Full-Circle Protractor

To measure an angle, set the center line of the protractor (0 and 180 degrees) at the point of the angle. Line up the center line with one leg of the angle. Look where the end of the other leg of the angle intersects with the curve of the protractor. That's the measure of the angle.

To draw an angle, begin with a straight line. Mark a point on the line. Set the center line of the protractor (0 and 180 degrees) at that point. Look at the degrees on the protractor, and use those measurements to mark the size of angle you want.

Remove the protractor. Use a ruler to draw a line through the mark you made and to the point you set on the original line.

2. *Construct a perfect right angle:*

A right angle is useful for all sorts of shapes and designs. It's an exact corner, formed by two perpendicular lines that meet at exactly 90 degrees. Here's how to construct a right angle without using a protractor:

1. Use your ruler to draw a straight line. Make a mark somewhere toward the center of the line. (You don't need to mark the exact center.) Label the mark *A*.

2. Place the metal tip of your drawing compass on point *A*. Open the compass an inch or so. (The exact distance doesn't matter as long as your line is long enough.)

    Swing an arc with the compass, and make a mark where it crosses toward the beginning of the line. Label that point *B*.

    Swing an arc in the other direction, and make a mark where it crosses toward the end of the line. Label that point *C*.

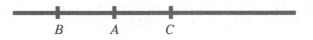

3. Open the compass wider, and place the tip on point *B*. Swing an arc and make mark above point *A*.

    Keep the compass at the same setting, and place the tip on point *C*. Swing an arc, and mark where the compass crosses the first arc. Label that point *D*.

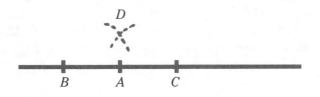

4. Line up your ruler, and draw a line exactly through points *A* and *D*.

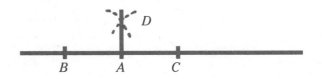

Angle *BAD* is a right angle, and so is angle *CAD*.

3. Construct a perfect equilateral triangle:

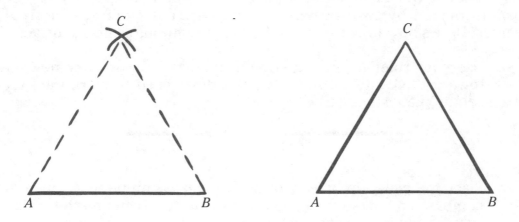

Constructing an Equilateral Triangle

You'll want to know how to construct triangles so that you can make fancy cats, New Mexican rainbirds, and all sorts of other designs. One of the most useful triangles is the equilateral triangle. An equilateral triangle has three angles of equal measure and three sides of equal length.

1. Draw a base line. Label one end of the line *A* and the other end *B*.
2. Place the metal tip of the compass at end A of the base line. Open your drawing compass to the length of the base line. Swing an arc, and make a mark above the center of the base line.

   Then place the tip of the compass at end *B* of the base line without changing the compass setting. Swing another arc. Mark the point where this arc crosses the first arc. Label that point *C*.
3. Draw lines from *A* to *C* and from *B* to *C*. Triangle *ABC* is an equilateral triangle with three equal sides and three equal angles.

4. Construct a perfect square:

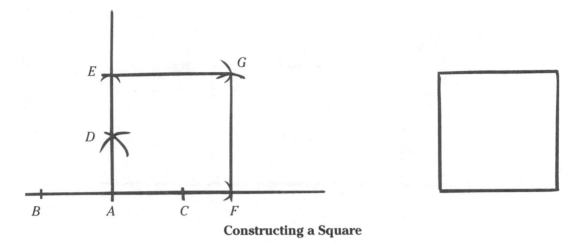

Constructing a Square

A square has four right angles and four equal sides. You can use this basic shape for all sorts of designs.

1. Construct a right angle, with points *A*, *B*, *C*, and *D*. Extend line *AD*.
2. Decide how large you want your square. Open your drawing compass to that size. For example, if you want a square that measures 2 inches × 2 inches, open your compass to 2 inches.

    Place the tip of the compass on point *A* of the right angle *CAD*. Swing an arc, and make a mark on the extended perpendicular line of the right angle and on the base line. Label the mark on the perpendicular line *E* and on the base-line *F*.
3. Keep the same setting on your compass. Put the tip on point *E*. Swing an arc, and make a mark above point *F*.
4. Keep the same setting. Put the tip on point *F*. Swing an arc, and make a mark that crosses the one you made in step 2. Label the crossing point *G*.
5. With your ruler draw a line between points *E* and *G*. With the ruler draw a line between points *G* and *F*. *AFGE* is a square.

5. Construct a perfect rectangle:

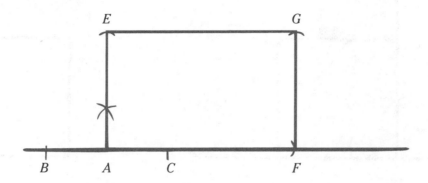

Constructing a Rectangle

A square is a particular sort of rectangle, a rectangle in which all the sides are equal.

You can make another sort of rectangle. This kind has two sides of one length and two sides of another length.

1. Follow the directions for constructing a square up to the place where you mark point *E* on the perpendicular line. Two sides of the rectangle will have the length from *A* to *E*.

   After you have set point *E*, open the compass to the length you want to use for the other two sides of the rectangle. Place the compass tip at point *A*. Swing an arc, and mark point *F* where the pencil crosses the base line.

2. Keep the same setting and place the compass tip at point *E*. Swing an arc, and make a mark above point *F*.

3. Use the compass to measure the distance from *A* to *E*. Place the compass tip on point *F*. Swing an arc, and make a mark that crosses the mark above *F*. Label the crossing point *G*.

4. Use your ruler to connect points *F* and *G*. Then connect *G* to *E*. *AFGE* is a rectangle.

GLOSSARY

Acre
A measurement for land, equal to 43,560 square feet. An acre is slightly smaller than a football field.

Arc
1. a portion of a curved line. 2. An unbroken, curved line between any two points on a circle.

Area
The amount of space inside a figure. Area is measured in square units, such as square feet, square miles, square centimeters, and square meters.

Atom
One of the basic particles of an element. Atoms connect or bond together into molecules. Atoms make up all elements in the universe.

Average
1. A number or value obtained by adding a set of quantities and dividing the sum by the number of quantities. The numbers or values can represent heights, distances, sizes, prices, and so on. 2. To find the average or mean, of a group of numbers. *Example:* $3 + 5 + 7 + 9 = 24 \div 4 = 6$.

Base
1. The bottom or lowest part of something. 2. The line or side on which a geometric figure rests. 3. A number raised to a power. *Example:* $10^2 = 100$, 10 is the base.

Centimeter
A unit of length in the metric system, equal to 0.01 or $1/100$ meter. One centimeter is about 0.394 inch.

Choreographer
A person who designs, composes, and arranges dances, especially for performing artists.

Circle
A closed curve equally distant from a fixed central point.

Circumference
The distance around a circle.

Combination
1. Something that is formed by joining or mixing together several things. 2. A sequence or order of arranging a set of objects or numbers when the order doesn't matter.

Cube
1. A boxlike figure that has six equal square faces. 2. The product of a number that is multiplied by itself two times. *Example:* $2 \times 2 \times 2 = 8$. Therefore the cube of 2 is 8.

Cycloid
The curve traced by a point on the circumference of a circle as the circle rolls along a straight line.

Degree
1. A unit for measuring angles or arcs of a circle. A whole circle has 360 degrees. 2. A unit for measuring temperature.

Diagonal
A straight line that joins two angles of a polygon that are not next to each other.

Diameter
A line segment connecting two points on a circle that passes through the center.

arc
radius
diameter
circumference
Circle

Cube

diagonal

Digit One of the numerals in a number, like a letter in a word. Any of the ten numerals from 0 to 9.

Dodecahedron A three-dimensional figure with 12 faces.

Equilateral triangle A three-sided figure in which all sides are the same length and all the angles are equal to 60 degrees.

Even number A number that can be divided by 2 without a remainder. *Example:* 4, 6, 8.

Foot A unit of length equal to 12 inches. Three feet make a yard. One foot is 0.3048 meter.

Fractal A shape or design that breaks into ever more complicated fragments while still maintaining the basic shape or design.

Hectare A measurement for land, equal to 10,000 square meters. One hectare is about 2,471 acres.

Hieroglyphics 1. Pictures or symbols that stand for words, numbers, or ideas. 2. The picture writing of the ancient Egyptians.

Hexagon A six-sided figure.

Hexagram A six-pointed figure or star.

Hexahedron A three-dimensional figure with six faces.

Horizontal Straight across, parallel to the horizon or a base line.

Hypotenuse The side of a right triangle that is opposite the right angle and is the longest side in the triangle.

Icosahedron A three-dimensional figure with 20 faces.

Inch A unit of length equal to $1/12$ foot. One inch is about 2.54 centimeters.

Infinity The quality of being without beginning or end and without limits. *Example:* There is an infinite series of numbers between any two numbers (between 0 and 1: $1/16$, $1/8$, $1/4$ and so on.)

Isosceles triangle A triangle that has two angles of equal measure and two sides of equal length.

Mean The mean is the same as the average.

Median The number or value in a series at which there are as many items above as there are below. The median is often compared to the average or mean, but is frequently not the same.

Meter 1. A unit of length in the metric system, equal to 100 centimeters. One meter is about 39.37 inches or $3^1/4$ feet. 2. A basic way of measuring the rhythm of poetry or music.

Metric system A system of measuring by 10's. The basic measure of length is the meter. The basic measures of weight are the gram and the kilogram. The basic measures of capacity are the milliliter and the liter.

Metrical foot A basic measure of rhythm for poetry or music.

Mile A unit of length equal to 5,280 feet. One mile is about 1,609 meters.

Millimeter A unit of length in the metric system, equal to 0.001 or $1/1000$ meter. One millimeter is about 0.039 inch.

Montage An artistic composition put together with different overlapping materials, designs, and parts of designs.

Mosaic A picture or design made by fitting together pieces of stone, tile, or glass.

Octahedron A three-dimensional figure with eight faces.

Octagon An eight-sided figure.

Octagram An eight-pointed figure or star.

Odd number	A number that cannot be divided evenly by 2. *Examples:* 1, 3, 5.
Parallel	Going in the same direction and always the same distance apart. Two parallel lines never meet or cross.
Parallelogram	A four-sided figure in which each pair of opposite sides is equal in length and each pair of opposite angles has equal measure.
Pentagon	A five-sided figure.
Pentagram	A five-pointed figure or star.
Percent	One part of a whole that has been divided into 100 parts. A percent compares a number to 100. For example, 15% means "15 out of 100."
Percentage	A part of a whole obtained by multiplying a number by a percent.
Perimeter	1. The boundary or rim of a figure or area. 2. The length of the boundary or rim.
Permutation	1. The act of changing the order of a set of objects or numbers. 2. An ordered arrangement of a set of objects. 3. A complete change in condition or character. *Example:* ABC can be arranged as; ABC, ACB, BCA, BAC, CAB or CBA.
Perpendicular	Straight up and down, at a right angle to a base line or surface.
Phi	1. The 21st letter of the Greek alphabet, written as Φ. 2.The formula for the golden proportion. The ancient Greeks named the formula for Phidias, the greatest of the ancient Greek sculptors, then shortened the name to phi.
Pi	1. The 16th letter of the Greek alphabet, written as π. 2. The ratio of the circumference to the diameter of any circle. Pi begins as 3.141592 and then goes on and on.
Place value	The value of a digit according to where it is located in a number. From right to left, the places in a number are the units or ones, tens, hundreds, thousands, ten thousands, hundred thousands, millions places and so on. *Example:* In the number 27, the digit 7 is in the units place, and the digit 2 is in the tens place.
Polygon	A closed two-dimensional figure bounded by straight lines. Polygons are named by the number of sides they have.
Polyhedron	A solid figure formed by 4 or more faces.
Prime number	A number greater than 1 and having only two factors. A prime number can be divided evenly by only two other numbers, 1 and itself. *Examples:* 2, 3, 5, 7.
Progression	A sequence of numbers in which each number is related to the other in the same way. Often the sequence is formed by adding, subtracting, multiplying, or dividing successive numbers in the same way. *Examples:* 1, 2, 3, 4... (+1), 1, 5, 25, 125,... (×5).
Proportion	The relationship of one part to another. The relationship may involve size, number, or amount. Four quantities, *a, b, c, d* are said to be in proportion if $a/b = c/d$.
Quadrilateral	A four-sided figure.
Radius	The part of a line from the center of a circle to a point on the circle. The plural of *radius* is *radii*.
Ratio	A comparison between two numbers or things. It is expressed as a quotient. Example: a/b or $a{:}b$.
Rectangle	A four-sided figure that has four (90-degree) right angles. A square is one type of rectangle.

Rhombus　A four-sided figure (a parallelogram) with four sides equal in length.

Right angle　An angle that measures 90 degrees.

Right triangle　A triangle that has one right (90-degree) angle.

Scalene triangle　A triangle in which all three sides are of different lengths and all three angles have different measures.

Square　1. A four-sided figure with four right angles and four sides of equal length. 2. The product of a number multiplied by itself. *Example:* $2 \times 2 = 4$. Therefore, the square of 2 is 4.

Square root　A number that, when multiplied by itself, will produce a particular number. The square root of 4 is 2.

Symmetry　A balance in size, shape, and arrangement. Parts can be balanced around a center or on each side of a line or lines.

Tesselation　The fitting of shapes together to form a design or picture. A mosaic. *Tesselation* comes from a Latin word that means "a small, square stone."

Tetrahedron　A three-dimensional figure with four sides.

Trapezoid　A four-sided figure in which only two sides are parallel.

Triangle　A figure with three sides and three angles.

Units　1. The single digits 1 through 9. 2. The ones position in a larger number, the place immediately to the left of the decimal point.

Vertical　Straight up and down.

Yard　A unit of length equal to 36 inches or 3 feet. One yard is about 0.91 meter.

INDEX

NOTES

NOTES

NOTES

NOTES